THE STRANGEST®

CRICKET

QUIZ

BOOK

First published in the United Kingdom in 2019 by
Portico
Pavilion Books Group Limited
43 Great Ormond Street
London
WC1N 3HZ

An imprint of Pavilion Books Company Ltd

ISBN 978-1-91162-218-5

A CIP catalogue record for this book is available from the British Library.

10 9 8 7 6 5 4 3 2 1

Reproduction by Mission Productions Ltd, Hong Kong
Printed and bound by Imak Offset, Turkey

This book can be ordered direct from the publisher at www.pavilionbooks.com

THE

STRANGEST®

CRICKET

QUIZ

BOOK

PORTICO

CONTENTS

INTRODUCTION

Welcome to *The Strangest Cricket Quiz Book.* I consider myself fortunate to have been given the opportunity to write this book, as the original *Cricket's Strangest Matches* (and several more of the *Strangest* series) was written by the estimable and prolific Andrew Ward. But here he is the victim of his own success, and while he is writing *The Strangest Football Quiz Book,* I have been lucky enough to be working on the cricketing equivalent. I have drawn on Andrew's fascinating book for about a third of the questions that follow, but have trawled cricket archives, libraries and websites for the remainder. Being free of the limitation of strange 'matches' has at least allowed me to include random moments of weirdness that have occurred both on and off the pitch.

Cricket, perhaps more than any other sport, lends itself to statistics – scores, bowling figures, partnerships, methods of dismissal etc. – and it seems almost every

day a statistic emerges to make you shake
your head in amazement: there are two
questions in the book about England's recent
Test series with India, and I write this
introduction having just heard of Durham's
amazing feat on 19 September 2018 of
beating their previous record lowest County
Championship score not once but twice in
one day, when scoring 61 and 66 against
Leicestershire. That would certainly have
made the cut had I been writing the book a
month later.

Naturally there is a focus on the extremes
of the game at the highest level around
the world: the biggest Test scores, feats of
wicket-taking and lamentable performances
with bat and ball. But Harold Pinter once
said, 'Drama happens in big cricket matches.
But also in small cricket matches.' So there
are questions about county cricket, village
cricket, and even some matches that took
place far from any recognised venue.

Some of the questions will be of matches and incidents familiar to the keen cricket follower, but some I defy anyone to answer without looking them up – I doubt I'd be able to answer half of them myself, even having compiled them. Rather than an orthodox quiz book, I hope the questions will instead stir fond memories and occasionally astonish you. So you'll discover who played in the shortest cricket match ever; who was cricket's worst night watchman; and how a ball of wool caused a Test career to be missed.

And because cricket reflects life, and laughter should be a part of everyone's life, I hope some of the questions will bring a smile to your face. If a handful of them are less than scrupulously backed up by the history books, I hope you (and Andrew) will forgive me.

'Cricket is battle and service and sport and art.'

Douglas Jardine
(1900–58)

1
LAMENTABLE EFFORTS

'Faster, Higher, Stronger'. That's the motto of the Olympic movement. And, quite frankly, as far as I'm concerned they can keep it. How boring is it just to watch people succeeding all the time? A more apt motto for cricket might be, 'Oh, God, not again …' Batting collapses, bowling disasters, fielding cock-ups, they all add to the fabric of cricket's rich tapestry, and the upside of this is that when good performances do come along, they stand out all the more, like diamonds among the dross.

'Ah, but you should accentuate the positive,' they say. Well, not here – not yet at least. Accentuating the negative is far more fun, so let's kick off with some pretty poor performances.

1 **WHY** were Northamptonshire particularly relieved in the 1930s that there was no relegation from the County Championship?

• •

2 **WHAT** was strange about Australia's total of 75 all out against South Africa in 1950?

3 **WHO** postponed his wedding in order to represent England at cricket in 1984, and why needn't he have really bothered?

• •

4 The tour to England by the West Indies in 1988 became known to English cricket fans as 'the summer of four ...' **WHAT?**

5 **WHY** did former Aussie captain Ian Chappell suggest that Graham Gooch should bowl spinner Phil Tufnell more, despite his underwhelming figures?

• •

6 'They wouldn't have got near them with another innings!' is a cry sometimes heard after a heavy defeat, but on the evidence of their two completed efforts, **HOW** many innings would Dera Ismail Khan have needed to reach Pakistan Western Railways' first innings total in 1964?

7 **HOW** many Northants batsmen reached double figures in their combined match total of 42 for 18 wickets (they were a man short) against Yorkshire in 1908?

---

8 **WHO** made the lowest score in the County Championship for 76 years when scoring 14 all out in 1983?

• •

9 **HOW** much did England lose by when they posted their record low Test innings of 45 all out in 1887?

---

10 It's never nice to get hit in the face by a fast delivery, especially in the days before helmets. In 1961 Gloucestershire captain Tom Pugh had his jaw broken in two places by Northamptonshire paceman David Larter. **WHAT** added insult to injury, to leave him most definitely shaken and stirred?

THE ANSWERS 96

2

MULTIPLE-CHOICE MADNESS

As I mentioned in the introduction, the chances of anyone getting all the questions in this book correct is pretty low. So I called to mind the story of the cricketer in a village game who is about to bat and confesses to his captain that he's overindulged in the pub at lunchtime and can now see three of everything. 'Don't worry,' says his skipper, 'just hit the middle ball, you'll be okay.' The batsman wanders confidently to the middle but is soon heading back to the pavilion after being clean-bowled. 'I told you to play the middle ball,' his exasperated captain said. 'I did,' came the reply, 'but I hit it with the wrong bat.' So I'll give you a chance with these – if you haven't a clue you can at least have a guess – just don't go for the middle one each time.

1 'The most disgusting incident I can recall in the history of cricket.' **WHAT** incident was being referred to?

(A) The 1932/33 Bodyline controversy.
(B) The sight of the streaking merchant seaman hurdling the stumps at Lord's in 1975.
(C) Dennis Lillee hurling his aluminium bat away in a Test match in December 1979.
(D) Something even worse ...

• •

2 **WHY** was a 3ft (1m) net installed around the boundary at Lord's for a match between MCC and Notts in 1900?

(A) A new scoring system was being trialled.
(B) To keep sheep off the pitch.
(C) To discourage crowd invasions.

3 **WHEN** E.W. Swanton complained that there was a woman in the Committee Room at Lord's, a fellow MCC member pointed out that it was the Saturday of the Test match and the visitor was in fact:

(A) The Archbishop of Canterbury
(B) Grayson Perry
(C) The Queen

4 'It's typical of English cricket. A tree gets in the way for 200 years and, when it falls down, instead of cheering, they plant a new one.' **WHICH** ground was Aussie David Gilbert referring to?

(**A**) Canterbury, Kent
(**B**) County Ground, Somerset
(**C**) New Road, Worcestershire

● ●

5 In 1907, George Dennett took 15 wickets in a single day for Gloucestershire against Northants, seven of them for ducks. **WHAT** else did he do in the match that was notable?

(A) Made a 'pair' himself.
(B) Helped bowl out the opposing team for just 12 runs in their first innings.
(C) Failed to finish on the winning side.

6 **WHY** did nine Derbyshire professional cricketers wear everyday clothes in a match vs Yorkshire in 1899, while their two amateur teammates wore official 'whites'?

(A) It was a protest against the demarcation between amateur 'gentlemen' and professional 'players'.
(B) It was a result of the gentlemen and the players changing in different dressing rooms.
(C) It was an early experiment in coloured clothing in cricket.

7 On 22 March 1902, Break O'Day went past Wellington's score in the single-innings decider of the Tasmanian championship in Australia. **WHEN** did their innings conclude?

(**A**) At once, of course.
(**B**) The next day, which would be strange.
(**C**) Two weeks later, which would be *really* strange.

● ●

8 Hampshire were bowled out for 15 (11 coming off the bat) in their first innings by Warwickshire in 1922. **HOW** many did they score when following on?

(**A**) 15 again
(**B**) 21
(**C**) 521

9 After almost being run out for nought, **WHICH** famous name made 385 out of 500 for Otago against Canterbury in New Zealand in December 1952, in the process personally outscoring the opposition's total from their two innings combined?

(**A**) Jack Hobbs
(**B**) Len Hutton
(**C**) Bert Sutcliffe

10 **WHAT** was strange about Middlesex spinner Jack Young's benefit match in August 1952?

(A) It was played against Arsenal FC.
(B) It was played under floodlights.
(C) It was 13-a-side.

• •

'He was bowled by a ball he would have done better to have left alone.'

Brian Johnston
(1912–94)

• •

THE ANSWERS ☞ 98

3

ABNORMAL ASHES

England and Australia have been playing one another at cricket since 1877, and the clashes have been dubbed the Ashes since 1882. They have thrown up some thrilling moments down the years: the runfests of the 1930s in England when innings seemed to last forever, interspersed with the brutal Bodyline series in Australia of 1932/33 that caused a rift between the Australian cricket board and the MCC; the thunderous bowling of 'Lilian Thomson' in the 1970s; and the seesaw series of the last decade or so, heralded by England's famous success in 2005. They have also seen their fair share of weird events.

1 It rained from midday onwards on the last day of the Headingley Ashes Test in 1975, but **WHAT** had already caused the abandonment of the match?

• •

2 Of **WHICH** legendary batsman did England's Jack Crapp remark, 'That bugger never had a tear in his eye throughout his whole life.'?

---

3 **WHO** made a Pratt of himself in the Trent Bridge Ashes Test in 2005?

• •

4 Len Hutton got away with it in 1951; Nasser Hussain didn't in 2002. Both disobeyed **WHICH** clichéd 'rule' of cricket?

---

5 **WHO** famously forgot Devon Malcolm after he made his Test debut for England against Australia in 1989?

• •

6 **WHAT** was Australian umpire Peter McConnell's helpful reply to Phil Tufnell when Tuffers asked him how many balls were left in the over at Melbourne in 1991?

7 **WHAT** were the odds on England winning the Headingley Ashes Test in 1981 at the end of the third day's play, and who famously backed them and ended up in profit?

8 Of **WHICH** Test series was Australian Jack Fingleton speaking when he said, 'I do not think there was one single batsman who played in most of those … games who ever afterwards recaptured his love for cricket.'?

9 In the Perth Ashes Test of 1979, **WHY** was the traditional sound of leather on willow missing, and why was there instead a series of clunks followed by a lump of metal whizzing through the air?

10 **WHOSE** wife, sitting in the crowd at Melbourne, supposedly bent down to pick up her knitting and missed her husband's entire Test batting career?

THE ANSWERS 102

4

IT'S NOT CRICKET!

Sledging has probably been a part of cricket since the first bowler squared up to the first batsman and questioned his parentage. It ranges from the threatening (Michael Clarke telling James Anderson to 'get ready for a broken arm'), to the slightly more subtle ('Hospital food suit you?' as Craig McDermott of Australia is supposed to have asked Phil Tufnell), to the funny (as when Merv Hughes enquired of Graham Gooch when he was struggling to lay a bat on anything, 'Would you like me to bowl a piano to see if you can play that?'). You could write a whole book about it (and in fact many people have).

But some questionable tactics go beyond the merely verbal, when the exhortation of Henry Newbolt to 'Play up! Play up! And play the game!' is entirely ignored and the spirit of cricket is most definitely not observed.

1 **WHY** did Leicestershire fast bowler Haydon Smith 'walk' when he didn't need to after edging a ball that landed just short of the Nottinghamshire wicketkeeper in 1928?

• •

2 And **WHO** famously didn't walk when he was caught at slip in an Ashes Test match at Trent Bridge in 2013, leading to much Antipodean gnashing of teeth and a parody recording of 'Under the Boardwalk' being made?

───────────────────────────────

3 Cricket had been played on the village green in Southwick, Sussex, for two centuries by the 1930s. In 1932 the local council regrettably had to prosecute five local cricketers for doing **WHAT** on the green?

(A) Playing cricket.
(B) Being drunk.
(C) Assaulting the greenkeeper.

• •

4 **HOW** did 11 Englishmen fluff their chance of a record payday in 2008, and what are the chances of the man who put up the money turning up at a cricket match in the foreseeable future?

5 Accidental collisions on the cricket pitch happen now and again as batsmen struggle to make their ground and fielders strive to throw down the stumps. **WHAT** was strange about the collision between Colin Croft and Fred Goodall in the Second Test between New Zealand and the West Indies in 1980?

6 In 2018 Minehead cricketer Jay Darrell was facing the bowling on 98 not out with 5 runs needed to win. A maiden century beckoned. One delivery later the match was won, and Darrell was still on 98. **WHAT** had happened?

7 **WHY**, officially, was Mike Gatting sacked as captain of England in 1988?

8 And **WHAT** did Gatting and many others suspect was the real reason for his dismissal?

9 **HOW** did Brian Rose's cunning Benson and Hedges Cup plan backfire in 1979?

10 And in a similar vein, **WHICH** village club in 2017 lost a match and as a result both won the league title and were relegated?

THE ANSWERS 105

5

RELUCTANT RECORD-BREAKERS

Just imagine the great sporting achievements of the last few years: Leicester City winning the Premier League title; Mark Johnston becoming the UK's most prolific flat racehorse trainer in 2018; the domination of cycling's grand tours recently by Britain's Wiggins, Froome, Thomas and Yates. Similarly, holding a cricketing record confers upon the player or team a kind of immortality … but sometimes it's one the record holder would prefer not to have.

1 Six international teams have scored 400-plus in their first innings and gone on to lose by an innings – or rather, it has happened on six occasions. **WHICH** team has performed the feat four times out of these six, including twice in the same month and three times inside a year?

● ●

2 **WHAT** record did Mark Taylor set in his first Test as captain of Australia in Karachi in 1994?

3 **WHAT** unwanted hat-trick did Australia achieve versus India in 2001?

● ●

4 **HOW** long would it have taken Sri Lanka's Roger Wijesuriya to bowl a team out single-handedly?

5 Sunil Ambris has so far only made two Test appearances for the West Indies, but each of his four innings have been notable, and he set two (unwanted) world firsts. **CAN** you remember them?

● ●

6 **WHO** is the only Test match opening batsman never to have been dismissed?

7 **WHO** has scored the most Test runs without recording a century?

8 Tony Lock, whose solitary wicket in the Old Trafford Test of 1959 probably prevented Jim Laker from taking all 20 rather than 'only' 19, scored over 10,000 runs in his first-class career. **BUT** how many centuries did he score?

• •

9 **WHAT** Test bowling record does England's Len Hopwood hold? Why might Ravi Bopara wish he had emulated him?

10 **WHAT** 'fastest' record does Glamorgan's Peter Judge hold?

THE ANSWERS 108

6

BRILLIANT AND BONKERS BOWLERS (1)

The bowler has a lot to think about when sending down his delivery. Don't bowl a no-ball; get your grip right; know where you're aiming it; make sure you've got the ball … Wait, what?

In September 2017 Jerome Taylor was bowling for the West Indies in a one-day international against England. He charged in, got to the crease and then shrugged apologetically and empty-handedly to England's David Willey who was on strike. For some inexplicable reason the ball then appeared from the umpire's pocket, like some cricketing magic trick.

Anyway, here are a selection of other impressive and interesting feats by bowlers, though, like Taylor, not always with the ball in hand.

1 **WHAT** links: Bhagwat Chandrasekhar (India, 242, 167); Chris Martin (New Zealand, 233, 123); Bruce Reid (Australia, 113, 93); Pragyan Ojha (India, 113, 89)?

• •

2 **WHAT** connects former Warwickshire spinner Ashley Giles to European royalty?

_____

3 **WHO** and, more strangely, in what capacity, told Lancashire and England's David Lloyd after witnessing his bowling at close quarters: 'I hope you don't mind me mentioning this, but you're the worst bowler I've ever seen.'

• •

4 **WHAT** is the probability of a county-standard bowler hitting a totally unprotected set of stumps from a normal delivery?

(A) 1 in 10
(B) 5 in 10
(C) 9 in 10

_____

5 Alan Smith, Warwickshire's captain and wicketkeeper, took two catches with the gloves in Essex's first innings against them in 1965. But when Trevor Bailey was caught behind in the second innings, Smith was on the field but Dennis Amiss took the catch. **WHY?**

6 **WHO** was the 'googly' – an off-break bowled with a leg-break action – named after?

(A) Bernard Google
(B) Bernard Bosanquet
(C) Bernard Gugenheim

• •

7 **WHY** did Fred Trueman come in to bat before Geoffrey Boycott for Yorkshire against Cambridgeshire in a Gillette Cup match in 1967?

_____

8 **WHY** did Javagal Srinath deliberately avoid taking a wicket by bowling wide of the stumps with Pakistan nine wickets down in a Test match in February 1999?

• •

9 **WHY** do many feel Graham Thorpe should have taken a leaf out of Srinath's book five months later?

_____

10 **HOW** did an encounter with a cricket ball prove decisive before play had even begun in the Edgbaston Ashes Test of 2005?

THE ANSWERS 111

7

BRILLIANT AND BONKERS BATSMEN (1)

Batting is arguably a lot harder than bowling. For a start, you only get one chance per innings. Make a mistake and you could be out first ball, with a long time to wait before you get the chance to put it right. Second, often the ball is either flying towards you at a terrific pace, or else has had spin imparted on it such that you can't be sure which direction it will go in once it's bounced. Commentating legend John Arlott summed it up well: 'No one is so lonely as a batsman facing a bowler supported by ten fieldsmen and observed by two umpires to ensure that his error does not go unpunished.'

With that in mind, here are some impressive and not-so-impressive landmarks from the gentlemen wielding the willow.

1 In 1979, England openers Mike Brearley and Geoff Boycott put together an opening partnership of 129 in 38 overs against the West Indies feared pace attack, a textbook Test match first-wicket stand. **WHY** were most England supporters watching tearing their hair out?

● ●

2 **WHO** reached a century in his final Test innings with a 5?

3 **WHAT** was possibly the most knee-jerk and unsuccessful 'promotion' in first-class cricket?

● ●

4 **WHY** did Lancashire's David Hughes sit in a darkened dressing room before going out to bat in the 1971 Gillette Cup semi-final against Gloucestershire?

5 **WHY** was Geoffrey Boycott under even more pressure than usual in his first Test match since ending his self-imposed exile at the Trent Bridge Ashes Test in 1977, and why might the home crowd have had mixed feelings about his first-innings century?

6 **WHAT** links: Andrew Jordan (1987/88), Hemulal Yadav (1997), Vasbert Drakes (2002), Andrew Harris (2003), Ryan Austin (2013/14) and no one else? You have 3 minutes to answer.

● ●

7 Of the above five, **WHO** was arguably out by the most?

8 **WHY** did former England captain Mike Atherton hold up his successor, Nasser Hussain, as providing a foolproof method of knowing what to do when you win the toss?

● ●

9 The Second Test between Australia and Pakistan at Melbourne in 1972/73 was quite strange in that Pakistan lost after declaring their first innings at 574–8, a lead of 133. But **WHAT** made the match a record-breaker?

10 **WHO** remonstrated with his teammates when they applauded a Dennis Amiss century for England at Trent Bridge in 1973: 'They're my runs you're clapping. *My runs!*'

THE ANSWERS 114

WHO SAID?

Cricket writing, whether in match reports or serious books, has always seemed to me to be a cut above other sports: consider Neville Cardus, C.L.R. James ('What do they know of cricket, who only cricket know?'), John Arlott, Matthew Engel, just to name a few. Perhaps it is the prolonged nature of the game, with reasonable intervals provided for reflection (whether intended, such as lunch or tea, or imposed by the weather), that has caused this. Whatever the reason, maybe some of this penchant for wordplay has rubbed off on the players, as cricket remains possibly the most quotable of sports. So I couldn't resist including a section of memorable utterances – I was tempted to include a googly by asking, 'Who said, "If your heart is in your dream, no request is too extreme"?', but resisted.* The first few are multiple choice to help you.

---

* It was Jiminy Cricket in *Pinocchio*.

1 **WHO** said, and of what country: 'Cricket civilises people and creates good gentlemen. I want everyone to play cricket in ———. I want ours to be a nation of gentlemen.'

(A) Donald Trump, USA.
(B) Nicola Sturgeon, Scotland.
(C) Robert Mugabe, Zimbabwe.

• •

2 **WHO** was Australia captain Ian Johnson referring to when he said at Old Trafford in 1956, 'It isn't fair. Look who you've got on your side.'

(A) Jim Laker
(B) Len Hutton
(C) God

---

3 **WHO** was greeted at the crease for his Test debut with these words: 'Bloody hell, who have we got here, Groucho Marx?'

(A) David Boon
(B) David Steele
(C) Asif Masood

4 About **WHICH** Test captain did the *New Age* newspaper make the following remark? 'His claim of being an all-rounder is clearly more a reflection of his physique than abilities.'

(A) Mike Gatting (England)
(B) Inzamam-ul-Haq (Pakistan)
(C) Khaled Mahmud (Bangladesh)

● ●

5 **WHY** didn't Greg Chappell accept that he was in poor form when questioned about a run of particularly low scores?

6 **WHO** said of whom that he appeared to be 'one canvas short of a full collection'? What was their finest hour together?

● ●

7 **WHAT** strange advice did maverick cricketer and captain Colin Ingleby-Mackenzie give to his Hampshire team before one match?

8 **WHO** described cricket as 'baseball on Valium'?

9 'I'm not a night watchman,' Robin Marlar reputedly said to his captain on his return to the pavilion after failing in the role in a match at the Oval in 1955. **HOW** did he supposedly spectacularly prove this?

• •

10 Phil Tufnell, who it's hard to imagine thundering in towards the batsman, once revealed the decisive factor in him becoming a spin bowler: 'You can't —— and bowl fast.' **WHAT** are the missing words?

• •

'Cricket is full of theorists who can ruin your game in no time.'

Ian Botham
(1955–)

• •

THE ANSWERS 117

9

MISCELLANEOUS STRANGENESS (1)

The more perceptive of you may have noticed how I have endeavoured to crowbar this collection of oddities into relevant sections. But with each section being limited to ten questions, one or two that might have gone elsewhere have found their way into this collection. And some of them just defy categorisation anyway. Where else, for instance, assuming that I could have squeezed it in, would I have placed a question about a man dressed as a giant cigarette interrupting play by continually wandering in front of the sightscreen at the Oval in 2007? (He had been hired as a promotional stunt to publicise the recent smoking ban, but by the end of the day the players must have been sorely tempted to light him up.) Here are some slightly more orthodox miscellaneous questions.

1 **WHAT** were the names of the teams that contested a match on the Gorak Shep plateau in 2009?

(**A**) Team Hillary vs Team Tenzing
(**B**) North Korea vs South Korea
(**C**) Buddhists vs Christians

---

2 When John Edrich told Geoffrey Boycott at the wicket in 1968 that he'd finally worked out how to play Australia's 'mystery spinner' John Gleeson, the Yorkshireman allegedly replied that he'd done the same two Tests earlier but urged Edrich not to tell 'those buggers up there'. **WHICH** buggers was he referring to?

• •

3 When Warwickshire's Bob Wyatt was bowling against Middlesex's Jack Robertson at Lord's, **WHY** did they and all the rest of the players suddenly throw themselves to the ground?

---

4 **WHY** was Gary Sobers feeling in a particularly generous mood in Trinidad in 1968?

5 **WHAT** have the following cricketers got in common: Joe Solomon (West Indies, 1961), Ashok Mankad (India, 1974), Dilip Vengsarkar (India, 1977) and Kevin Pietersen (England, 2007)?

● ●

6 In a case of nominative determinism, Yorkshire and England's Brian Close was well known for fielding almost suicidally close to the batsman, back in the days before protective equipment. On one occasion he was fielding at forward short leg and a well-hit shot cannoned off his forehead and was caught at first slip. His teammates were jubilant but one concerned colleague was moved to ask Close, 'But Brian, what would have happened if that shot had hit you right between the eyes?' **WHAT** was his response?

───────────────────────────────

7 By August 2018, over 2,300 Test matches had been played in total, with only two finishing as ties, where both sides' innings are completed with the scores standing equal. In the first tied Test, between Australia and the West Indies in 1960, Australia lost four wickets in the last two overs chasing victory and three of the dismissals were in the same manner. **WHAT** was it?

● ●

8 Australia have in fact featured in both of the only two tied matches in Test history, in 1960 and 1986. **WHICH** Aussie was involved directly in both matches?

9 In the Oval Test match in 2006, Pakistan captain Inzamam-ul-Haq led his team onto the field to resume play only to find no one to play against … and yet the match was awarded to England and Inzamam ended up being suspended. **WHY** was this, and which other person involved in the Test also picked up a ban?

10 **WHICH** year were declarations introduced in first-class cricket?

'The aim of English Test cricket is, in fact, mainly to beat Australia.'

**Jim Laker
(1922–86)**

BIZARRE
BOOK TITLES

Is there a more depressing sight than when you pick up a book in the sporting section of a bookshop and the title reads: *Joe Bloggs: My Autobiography*? You immediately and instinctively know without opening the cover that the chances of reading anything more interesting than 'Then we played X and then we played Y and we won the title, it felt great ...' are smaller than Kevin Pietersen being invited to become the chairman of the England and Wales Cricket Board. I think this trend is dying out, to be honest, as publishers realise they need to entice the reader in, and I must admit that there are more than a few duds on the shelves with interesting titles, but at least you feel that someone has made an effort, if only on the front cover.

So, with no particular recommendation or criticism from me, other than to say that I've read numbers four and five and regretted neither, can you identify the **AUTHORS** of these books about cricket or cricketers? I've given you the initials and the date to help.

1 *Ten for 66 and All That* (A.M., 1958)

• •

2 *Third Man to Fatty's Leg* (S.J., 2004)

━━━━━━━━━━━━━━━━━━━━━━━━━━━━━━━━━━━

3 *Blood, Sweat and Treason* (H.O., 2010)

• •

4 *Fibber in the Heat* (M.J., 2012)

━━━━━━━━━━━━━━━━━━━━━━━━━━━━━━━━━━━

5 *Penguins Stopped Play* (H.T., 2006)

• •

6 *Life Beyond the Airing Cupboard* (J.B., 2008)

━━━━━━━━━━━━━━━━━━━━━━━━━━━━━━━━━━━

7 *My Autobiography (Don't Tell Kath)* (I.B., 1994)

11

STRANGE GOINGS-ON AT THE VILLAGE GREEN

I don't know about you, but I can't drive past a village cricket ground without feeling a pang of disappointment that there is no match taking place, even if it's pouring with rain or the field is covered in snow. Likewise, the thrill I feel when I do catch a fleeting glimpse of 'flannelled fools' (as Kipling called them) is indescribable. Never mind that most village teams are seldom at full strength, someone will always have forgotten some or all of their kit, and the standard of umpiring can be questionable (a visiting batsman once said to the umpire after a particularly wayward delivery, 'Don't you think that was wide?' only to receive the reply, 'You're right, I don't think I've ever seen one wider'), if we ever lose village cricket it would be the sporting equivalent of the ravens leaving the Tower of London.

The cricket XIs that illuminate the questions below might not all be village teams by a strict definition, but you get the idea …

1 When the entire Eynsham team suddenly left the field in the middle of Wantage's innings in 2001, **WHICH** Alfred Hitchcock film most accurately describes why?

(A) *Stage Fright*
(B) *To Catch a Thief*
(C) *The Birds*

• •

2 In a 1936 charity match in Wittersham, a village XI played against a professional team handicapped by a lack of numbers, but the pros still won. **HOW** many were on the professional team?

━━━━━━━━━━━━━━━━━━━━━━━━━━━━

3 In 1994 in a village cricket match, Clive Scott made 91 not out. **WHO** did he blame for his failure to get a century?

(A) The umpire
(B) His wife
(C) The BBC weather forecast

• •

4 **WHAT** was the batsman's reply to the following (almost certainly apocryphal) exchange at a village cricket match?

Batsman: That was never out!
Umpire: You look in the local paper next week and it'll be out.
Batsman: No, you look! I'm ——.

5 **HOW** did every wicket fall in the 2006 match between Dishforth and Goldsborough? And what was even stranger about them all?

---

6 **WHY** was floodlighting essential for the match played between local rivals Threlkeld and Caldbeck in Cumbria in 2013?

• •

7 When Yatton bowled out 'The Farmers' for 92 in 1887, **HOW** many ducks were recorded in the Farmers' innings? (Clue: there were 8 extras scored.)

(A) None
(B) Less than five
(C) Ten or more

---

8 Future England captain Percy Chapman dominated the batting in a 12-a-side game in 1925. His 11 teammates scored 7 runs between them. **HOW** many did Percy score?

9 **WHY** are cricket matches at Bramble Bank limited to a maximum of two hour-long fixtures per year?

....

10 **WHY** was the bowling in an 1878 Cambridge 'Town vs Gown' match restricted to 'lobs only'?

....

'I understand cricket – what's going on, the scoring – but I can't understand why.'

Bill Bryson
(1951–)

THE ANSWERS 124

12

WHAT HAPPENED NEXT?

You know what cricket can be like. Everything is going along perfectly normally and then something odd happens. In 2011, for instance, England's Ian Bell was run out to the last ball before tea in a Test match with India. What happened next was that after the tea interval Bell resumed his innings. He'd been run out while having a chat in the middle of the pitch to congratulate Eoin Morgan on the lovely boundary he'd just hit. The only trouble was, unbeknown to them the ball hadn't actually quite gone for 4. Even the fielder didn't realise this, so it came as quite a shock to most people when the wicketkeeper removed the bails and appealed when the ball was returned to him. It all left a sour taste, but over tea the India captain Mahendra Singh Dhoni sportingly agreed to withdraw the appeal, and Bell carried on.

Anyway, in what is certainly not a shameless attempt to piggyback onto the popularity of a well-known BBC sports quiz, I thought it would be fun to have a section devoted to just such incidents.

1 **WHAT** happened to Graeme Fowler while at the crease on 149 not out against India in 1985?

---

2 Australia vs Sri Lanka, First Test, Kandy, 1999. A Mahela Jayawardene top edge sailed up in the air, and there was not one but two Aussie fielders within range to catch it. **WHAT** happened next?

· ·

3 **WHAT** happened after Geoff Boycott scored his Test best 246 not out for England against India at Headingley in 1967?

---

4 England were 17–3, just over an hour into a 1998 Test match against West Indies at sunny Sabina Park, Kingston. **WHAT** happened next?

· ·

5 **WHAT** happened after Pakistan made Australia follow on in Karachi in 1988? And what didn't happen again until 2005 at Trent Bridge?

6 When Surrey reached 92–3 in their first innings against Worcestershire in 1954, **WHAT** did their captain Stuart Surridge do?

(A) Insisted on the sightscreen being repainted.
(B) Declared.
(C) Had a brainwave about a new design of cricket bat.

---

7 **WHAT** happened when an amateur cricketer, a 26-year-old schoolteacher making his debut for Glamorgan, came to the crease at 114–9 against South Africa facing a hat-trick?

(A) He came to the wicket wearing sunglasses and immediately appealed against the light.
(B) He scored a half-century and saved the match.
(C) He took guard outside leg stump to avoid the hostile bowling.

8 **WHY** did England captain Monty Bowden decide to stay in South Africa after playing for England there in 1889? And why did it turn out to be the wrong decision?

9 **WHAT** happened after Zimbabwe's captain Heath Streak won the toss in the Perth Test match against Australia in October 2003?

10 England scored an impressive 477 in their first innings in Chennai in 2016. **WHAT** happened next?

· ·

'If cricket is all
that you know, then you
would not be a great
commentator.'

Harsha Bhogle
(1961–)

· ·

THE ANSWERS 127

13

ODI? OH DEAR ...

If a Test match is a five-course meal, a one-day match is a fish-and-chip takeaway; goodness knows what that makes a T20 – a guilty jam doughnut, perhaps? I'm with the unidentified journalist who said of T20 at its launch in 2003, 'This'll never catch on.' The first ever one-day international was an ad hoc affair in 1971 hastily arranged after the Third Test between Australia and England was washed out. Australia won a 40-over match by five wickets. Despite reaching the final on three occasions, England have never won the Cricket World Cup in 11 attempts, compared to Australia's record five wins, but will be hoping that the home advantage conferred in 2019 will help them break that particular duck.

With all the dashing around and frantic run-chases, one-day internationals give plenty of scope for cricketing chaos, even before you have to whip out the pocket calculator.

1 **WHY** will no one believe anything Pakistan coach Mansoor Rana says after his U-19 team sensationally won the 2006 World Cup after setting India a target of just 110 to win in the final (India were then skittled out for 71 in 18.5 overs)?

• •

2 **WHAT** strange ODI 'double' is held by Sri Lanka's Sanath Jayasuriya?

───────────────────────────────────

3 The career of one of the greats of the game, Sir Garfield Sobers, famous for his swashbuckling 36 runs in one over, overlapped only briefly with the introduction of one-day international cricket. **WHAT** was his ODI batting average?

• •

4 **HOW** many balls did England have in hand when they beat Canada in the 1979 World Cup?

───────────────────────────────────

5 **WHICH** of these 'Associate nations' has beaten England in an ODI or T20 international?

(A) Ireland
(B) Scotland
(C) The Netherlands

6 When West Indies played Ireland in a one-day game in Londonderry in 1969, their last two batsmen more than doubled the score. **HOW** many were the Windies all out for?

● ●

7 **WHAT** lasting effect has mathematician Tony Lewis had on limited-overs cricket?

8 And **WHY** did South Africa wish he'd been around in 1992?

● ●

9 And **WHY** might it not have done them any good anyway if the 2003 World Cup is anything to go by?

10 **WHO** accepted the umpires' offer of bad light and confidently marched off the field only to find they'd lost the match?

THE ANSWERS 129

14

COUNTY CRICKET

It sometimes seems as though the English County Championship exists in its own vacuum, especially in these days of wall-to-wall international cricket and central contracts, meaning that England's elite cricketers can only turn out for their county when the England and Wales Cricket Board thinks it's a good idea, which in practice means hardly ever. England captain Joe Root made just three appearances for Yorkshire in the summer of 2018 and played in seven Test matches. With all the attention on the national team, county cricket is expected to churn out Test-quality players for England and provide Test-quality grounds to play on. Yet still it keeps going, synonymous with John Major's 'long shadows on county grounds'.

So does anything strange happen in county cricket, a sedate competition observed by the customary one man and his dog? Well, if you happened to be at Southport in 1982 …

1 In the match between Lancashire and Warwickshire in 1982, **WHAT** strange thing happened when Graeme Fowler batted?

• •

2 In the match between Lancashire and Warwickshire in 1982, **WHAT** strange thing happened when Gladstone Small was called up mid-match to act as cover for England?

3 In the match between Lancashire and Warwickshire in 1982, **WHAT** strange thing happened when Les McFarlane bowled a hat-trick ball?

• •

4 In the match between Lancashire and Warwickshire in 1982, **WHAT** strange thing happened after Warwickshire opened the match by scoring 523–4 declared?

5 **WHAT** strange thing happened in Northamptonshire's first innings in a county match against Leicestershire in 1967? And **WHY** did Jack Birkenshaw feel left out?

6 Ian Botham took 12 wickets in the match and the side following on won a narrow victory. **WHERE** and **WHEN** was the game played?

• •

7 In a three-day match versus Derbyshire at Buxton in June 1975, Lancashire made 477–5 declared on the first day. **WHY** was no play possible on the second day?

_____

8 **WHY** did George Gunn give his wicket away in a county match for Nottinghamshire against Glamorgan?

(A) He was a traditionalist.
(B) He was bloody-minded.
(C) He was hungry.

• •

9 **WHY** were Leicestershire fielders constantly running into position between overs in the first innings of an end-of-season match against Lancashire in 1983, and **WHY** did they open the bowling with David Gower in the second innings?

_____

10 'Ladies and gentlemen, a correction to your scorecards: for "F.J. Titmus", read "Titmus, F.J.".' **WHY** did the announcer at Lord's feel it necessary to correct what seems a trivial error?

THE ANSWERS 131

15

DUCKS GALORE!

Can there be anything more humiliating for a batsman than to be out for a 'duck-egg' (referring to the similarity between the egg and the figure '0' – a similar comparison is believed to be why zero at tennis is called 'love', from the French *l'oeuf*)? The term was apparently first used in cricket in an 1866 newspaper article describing the Prince of Wales's lack of success with the bat. It would surely be a brave umpire that would give him out LBW, presumably, although a butler officiating in his employer's cricket match had to make just such a delicate decision on a run-out, before diplomatically announcing, 'His Lordship is not in.'

Returning to the question of ducks, you are said to bag a pair of ducks if you are out for nought in both innings; a golden duck is when you're out first ball; and a diamond duck occurs when a batsman is run out without facing a ball.

Here, then, is a collection of questions about those batsmen who failed to trouble the scorers.

1 **WHY** would a duck have been hard to swallow for John Inverarity in a match between Western Australia and South Australia in the 1969/70 season?

• •

2 When Border (the South African region, not the Australian player) scored a paltry 34 in their two innings against Natal in 1959 (still a record low first-class aggregate), **HOW** many ducks did they collect?

3 When Aussie bowler Alan Hurst supposedly asked why he was batting at No. 11 again, **WHAT** was the reply?

• •

4 **WHAT** was strange about Josh Hazlewood's duck for Australia versus New Zealand in a one-day international in 2017?

5 **WHAT** links Bob Holland (Australia, 1985), Ajit Agarkar (India, 1999/2000) and Mohammad Asif (Pakistan, 2006)?

6 Marvan Attapattu scored 16 centuries and amassed 5,504 runs in his Test career for Sri Lanka, but **HOW** many runs did his first six innings yield, and **HOW** did an umpire's marginal call prevent him breaking a cricketing record?

• •

7 **WHO** is the only person to have collected two diamond ducks in Test cricket?

---

8 **WHO** has scored more pairs in Test matches than any other cricketer?

• •

9 Of batsmen who have played 20 Tests or more, **WHO** has the lowest batting average?

---

10 **WHO** has scored the most ducks in Test match history?

THE ANSWERS 133

STRANGE SAYINGS

Many years ago *Private Eye* dubbed sports commentators' howlers 'Colemanballs', after the late great David Coleman. Almost certainly the most famous cricketing one is Brian Johnston's 'The bowler's Holding, the batsman's Willey', which everyone who was around at the time (1976) insists never happened. Nevertheless, I can't be the only person who has heard the account so often that I have convinced myself I actually heard it live – I certainly prefer to think so. All I can say is that if the arch-punster Johnston ever *had* used those words, it would not have been by mistake! Whether my other favourite cricketing Colemanball is apocryphal or not I have been unable to find out, but it is reported that when one batsman resumed after receiving lengthy treatment for a nasty blow to an unmentionable part of his anatomy from the penultimate delivery of the over, the commentator remarked: 'And he's going to carry on ... one ball left.'

David Coleman wasn't really a cricket reporter, but can you **MATCH** the cricketing Colemanballs here to the commentator/pundit/player?

1 'England win by a solitary 9 runs.'

2 'I'm not one to blame anyone, but it was definitely Viv Richards' fault.'

3 'On the first day Logie decided to chance his arm and it came off.'?

4 'I hurt my thumb and then obviously the mother-in-law died.'

5 'And I can see the strong wind blowing the sun towards us.'

6 'There's Kallicharran chasing after it, his legs going even faster than he is.'

7 'The Queen's Park Oval, exactly as its name suggests – absolutely round.'

---

8 'He's played the shot of the day twice now.'

• •

9 'He's a very good cricketer. Pity he's not a better batter or bowler.'

---

10 'If Gower had stopped that it would have decapitated his hand.' Choose from:

Trevor Bailey
Henry Blofeld
Frank Bough
Tony Cozier
Farokh Engineer
Graeme Fowler
Mike Gatting
Tom Graveney
Brian Johnston
Fred Trueman

THE ANSWERS 135

17

MISCELLANEOUS STRANGENESS (2)

Sidney Poitier once said, 'So much of cricket, it seems to me, is determined by pure randomness.' Well, actually he said 'life' instead of 'cricket', but I think he was on to something. I find hard to believe the story about the dismissal of Colin Wells in a match between Sussex and Warwickshire in 1981, when he was supposedly run out by a fashion statement. Apparently, Geoff Humpage was bowling when a straight drive by Wells's batting partner eluded Humpage's outstretched hand but couldn't avoid the massive flares of the Warwickshire bowler, which deflected the ball onto the stumps and ran out Wells backing up. If you'd asked Humpage that morning when he was pulling on his bell-bottoms to predict their significance later that day he'd have shrugged his shoulders. Wells must have wished he'd taken a pair of scissors to them.

On which point, here is another set of stand-out random events.

1 **WHY** did England bowler and tail-ender David Allen block the last two balls of a Test with West Indies in 1963 to protect his batting partner, a skilled batsman who would end his career with 22 Test centuries?

● ●

2 In the Fourth Test between West Indies and India in Jamaica in 1976, **HOW** many different players did India field in the match due to injuries? And **WHY** was Surinder Amarnath's departure different from the rest?

3 In 1977 the Centenary Test was played in Melbourne between Australia and England to commemorate the very first Test match, played (naturally) in 1877 at the same venue between the two teams. Australia won by 45 runs (Australia 138 and 419–9 dec., England 95 and 417). **WHAT** was so strange about that?

● ●

4 In that Centenary Test England's Derek Randall scored a wonderful 174 in England's vain run chase. **WHAT** song did he repeatedly sing to himself to the bemusement of the Australian bowlers?

5 **WHO** did England 'flippin' murder' in a Test match just before Christmas 1996? And **WHAT** was the unique result of the contest?

6 **WHAT** strange occurrence happened behind the stumps when England played New Zealand at Lord's in 1986?

• •

7 **WHY** did Larry Gomes have cause to be extremely grateful to Malcolm Marshall at Headingley in July 1984?

8 **WHAT** historic role did New Zealand's Doug Cowie play in the Third Test between New Zealand and England in Auckland in 2002?

• •

9 In **WHAT** ingenious way did W.G. Grace once supposedly try to avoid a dismissal being recorded against him?

10 **WHICH** stand-in England captain was dismissed by one future England captain on the instructions of another future England captain?

THE ANSWERS 136

18

HISTORY MAKERS

In the sense that 'first-class cricket' (matches of at least three days' scheduled duration with each team having the opportunity to play two innings) was only officially defined in May 1894, you could argue that the game is less than 125 years old. But seeing as the first written reference to cricket (or at least 'creckett') is from 1597, I think we can safely assume it has a somewhat longer history. Two gentlemen were jailed in 1611 for playing cricket on the Sabbath instead of going to church, but it seems that cricket really took off in Restoration England, when it became a prime target for gamblers – *plus ça change*. The first written code of laws was laid down in 1744. Although matches between counties became increasingly commonplace in the years that followed, the first official county championship season was in 1890, and was won by Surrey.

So, history lesson over, here are some questions about players or teams that have left their mark on the game in the last hundred or so years.

1 After starting the match with a not-bad 221 in their first innings against Victoria in 1926, **HOW** many did New South Wales need to avoid an innings defeat when they began their second innings?

(A) 686
(B) 786
(C) 886

• •

2 In the same match, **WHOSE** best figures were also worst figures?

3 **WHAT** was Devon Malcolm's accurate prediction after being hit on the head by Fanie de Villiers in the 1994 Oval Test against South Africa?

• •

4 In 2006, Sri Lanka lost their first two wickets for only 14 runs. **HOW** many runs did Jayawardene and Sangakkara put on for the third wicket?

5 **WHAT** strange double did John Prodger of Kent achieve in Kent's second innings against Middlesex in 1963?

6 **WHAT'S** the shortest completed cricket match ever played?

....

7 **WHY** might Surrey's Pat Pocock have found it difficult to get into a consistent rhythm when bowling the final over of Sussex's second innings at Eastbourne in 1972?

8 **WHY** is Sri Lankan Clive Inman's world record fastest half-century (8 minutes) for Leicestershire versus Nottinghamshire in 1965 looked on with some disdain?

....

9 Tied matches, where both teams have scored the same number of runs and the side batting last has completed its innings, are strange occurrences – on average it happens about once every two years throughout all first-class cricket matches around the world. But **HAS THERE** ever been a tied match where both teams have scored identical first and second innings totals to each other?

10 An unusual means of dismissal is to be given out 'obstructing the field'. **WHO** is the only player to be given out twice for this?

19

DAFT DESCRIPTIONS

As I've mentioned before, I think cricket lends itself to description via the written word, and the same applies to the spoken word. In both instances journalists and commentators are trying to get across what they have seen or are seeing to someone who is only listening or reading, and that includes the atmosphere. So when Henry Blofeld goes on about how many buses are coming down the Harleyford Road, or the vapour trail from a passing jet, or a plastic bag blowing across the outfield, although some wish he would get back to the match, for many it conjures up memories of a day spent joyfully at the cricket, whether in the near or distant past.

And when it comes to the action itself, commentators and journalists alike are always trying to come up with fresh ways of painting a word-picture of what they are looking at – and sometimes the results can be pretty abstract.

1 **WHOSE** bowling run-up was described by Martin Johnson as like 'Someone in high heels and a panty-girdle chasing a bus'?

2 **WHOSE** run-up did Frank Keating say reminded him of 'A 1914 biplane tied up with elastic bands trying vainly to take off'?

3 **WHICH** England bowler was described by Vic Marks as 'The enigma with no variation'?

4 **WHOSE** batting did John Arlott say was 'Like an old lady poking with her umbrella at a wasps' nest'?

5 **WHO** did Matthew Engel suggest batted 'Like an octopus with piles'?

6 WHOSE stance when getting onto his tiptoes to play a shot was described by Navjot Srinath as 'Like a dwarf at a urinal'?

• •

7 WHOSE unsuccessful attempt to avoid falling on his stumps was likened to 'An elephant trying to do the pole vault'?

8 And WHOSE similarly abortive effort not to suffer the same fate supposedly led to a 2-mile (3.5km) traffic jam in 1991?

• •

9 WHO said to whom, of his moustache, 'The last time I saw anything like that on a top lip, the whole herd had to be destroyed!'

10 WHOSE bowling action was likened by Mike Gatting to 'A frog in a blender'?

THE ANSWERS 142

20
VENTURING OUTSIDE FIRST-CLASS CRICKET

Minor Counties, club cricket, charity matches – when you think of all the cricket that gets played up and down the country and around the world every week that doesn't get reported on, it makes you frustrated that there must have been so many strange occurrences that happen that no one knows about outside the participants. This anonymity occasionally works in someone's favour, as in the strange case of Adrian Shankar, a wannabe first-class cricketer who was having trouble convincing counties that his game was up to scratch. A tarted-up CV with three years knocked off his age plus a few impressive achievements in a fictitious Sri Lankan tournament later and Shankar had a two-year contract with Worcestershire and was thrown into their injury-hit team for his one and only first-class fixture. His lies were revealed soon after and Worcestershire cancelled his contract. When asked about the discrepancy in his age, Shankar explained that he had spent the first three years of his life on a life-support machine, so they obviously didn't count!

Fortunately for us, some of the odd and impressive moments outside first-class cricket have been recorded.

1 The top scorer in Cheshire's second innings of a Minor Counties match against Dorset in 1988 scored 56 out of his 69 in a single over thanks to a vicar. **HOW?**

●●●●●●●●●●●●●●●●●●●●●●●●●●●●●●●●●●●●●●●

2 In 2015 Liam Livingstone, who has since gone on to play T20 cricket for England, hit 350 from 138 balls for Nantwich against Caldy in a 45-over match. Out of his 27 sixes, 16 were hit into the 'dead centre of town' – **HOW** did he achieve this?

3 Poor old Ross County travelled across to Elgin for a single-innings match in 1964 and had to play a man short. In some matches this could mean the difference between victory and defeat, but **HOW** close did Ross County get to Elgin's 145–5 declared?

●●●●●●●●●●●●●●●●●●●●●●●●●●●●●●●●●●●●●●●

4 In 1891, in a single-innings match, Grace top-scored with 81 and also made three ducks. Meanwhile, Robinson took all ten wickets and all three catches, only one of which was a caught and bowled. **HOW?**

5 In a double-wicket contest at Rickmansford in May 1827, two 'gentlemen' from Middlesex were **BEATEN** by a man partnered by:

(A) His great-grandfather
(B) His wife
(C) His dog

6   **WHO**, in 1967, took nine wickets in consecutive balls and was then taken out of the attack?

•••••••••••••••••••••••••••••••••••••••

7   **WHY** was it generally not a good idea to annoy West Indian fast bowler Roy Gilchrist?

─────────────────────────────────────

8   Trooper Holland was bowled *by* a maiden for a duck in a veterans' charity match at Trent Bridge in 1907. Of **WHICH** military exploit was he a survivor?

(A) Charge of the Light Brigade (1854)
(B) Battle of Rorke's Drift (1879)
(C) Relief of Mafeking (1900)

•••••••••••••••••••••••••••••••••••••••

9   **WHY** isn't it so strange that the FFOP cricket team have played matches in venues including uninhabited islands, Vatican City, and on a specially constructed pitch straddling the Dutch–Belgian border?

─────────────────────────────────────

10   In 1939 Bermudan Alma Hunt took seven wickets before opening the batting and facing just over two-thirds of the bowling in Aberdeenshire's ten-wicket victory over West Lothian. **HOW** many runs did his partner score?

THE ANSWERS 144

WHAT'S IN A NAME?

Sometimes the names on a cricket scorecard are entertaining even before any scores have been added. There is a story – probably untrue, sadly – about the England cricket team of the 1940s that contained Alec Bedser and Jack Crapp. Reporting late to the team's Leeds hotel for a Test match at Headingley, Jack went up to the receptionist who automatically asked him, 'Bed, sir?' 'No, Crapp,' answered Jack, to which the receptionist replied, 'Second door on the left, sir.' If you find that funny, then like me you probably found it difficult to keep the smirk off your face during India's tour of England in 2018 whenever Bumrah, Pant and Hardik were on the field. Carry on Cricket, indeed … On a more elevated note, there really is a cricketing Napoleon Einstein who played for India Under-19s.

To the questions:

1 **WHICH** of these three characters represented Surrey and an All-England XI in the 1850s?

(A) Frederick Bowler Caesar
(B) Julius Caesar
(C) Mark Anthony

2 **WHICH** of these future England captains had their debut Test scores contained in their surname?

(A) Graham G00ch
(B) Alistair C00k
(C) Joe R00t

3 **WHAT** poetically perfect dismissal occurred in the Brisbane Ashes Test in 1979?

4 And **WHICH** of these three dismissals never happened?

(A) Cook, c. Mustard, b. Onions
(B) Lee, c. Lee, b. Lee
(C) Lamb, c. Curry, b. Rice

5 Of **WHICH** Sri Lankan cricketer did David Lloyd say: 'Imagine if you got him on a triple-word score in Scrabble'?

---

6 In 1907, three very famous individuals scored 10 runs between them in a match at Lord's. **CAN** you identify them from their initials?

A.C.D.
A.A.M.
P.G.W.

••

7 **WHAT** uniquely happened to Vijay Ananda Gajapathi Raju, otherwise known as the Maharajkumar of Vizianagram, during India's tour of England in 1936?

---

8 And while on the subject of anagrams (pay attention), **WHICH** Test batsman's surname is an anagram of 'cricket shot'?

••

9 And **WHICH** butter-fingered cricketer was sometimes known as 'Parmesan Tony' for similar anagrammatical reasons?

10 Edwin Alletson scored 189 batting at number nine for Notts against Sussex in 1911. **WHAT** was his middle name?

(A) Boaler
(B) Battman
(C) Ffylder

● ●

'It has been said of the unseen army of the dead, on their everlasting march, that when they are passing a rural cricket ground, the Englishmen fall out of ranks for a moment to lean over a gate and smile.'

J.M. Barrie
(1860–1937)

THE ANSWERS 146

22

BEYOND THE BOUNDARY

Not everything strange connected with cricket is confined to the field of play. For instance, after the Second World War, Surrey County Cricket Club needed a new captain – and the chap had to be an amateur, of course. In due course it was decided to offer the post to Major Leo Bennett, who had turned out for the Second XI before the war and impressed in matches during the conflict as well. As it turned out, a certain Major *Nigel* Bennett was also a Surrey member and had also turned out for the Seconds some ten years' earlier, though he was considered a significantly inferior player. You can probably guess what's coming. Somehow Nigel was offered the job of county captain instead of Leo and, somewhat surprised but embracing the can-do spirit of the British Army, he said, 'Yes, please.' His appointment was not a success. He finished the season with a batting average of 16, took one wicket and his captaincy was described as 'utterly lost'.

Let me ask you about some more incidents that took place either off the field or during a break in play.

1 The unique attitude to cricket of Hampshire captain Colin Ingleby-Mackenzie can perhaps be summed up by his instructions to his players before a night out: 'I absolutely insist that all my boys are in before ...'
WHEN?

---

2 **WHAT'S** perhaps the most extreme reaction to being dropped from a cricket team?

(A) Setting fire to the cricket HQ
(B) Scoring a double century
(C) Retiring

• •

3 **WHAT** unfortunate fate did England batsman Colin Milburn share with England goalkeeper Gordon Banks?

---

4 Two Weetabix soaked in milk for exactly 8 minutes; one teabag to last a whole Test match; a floppy hat that was defended to the hilt. **WHO?**

• •

5 **WHAT** crucial part did Matthew Hoggard play in England's 2000 victory over Pakistan in Karachi, despite not featuring in the team?

6 **WHY** did Essex's Peter Smith report to the Oval for duty against the West Indies in 1933 despite not being picked by England?

---

7 **WHAT** cricketing first did merchant seaman Michael Angelow achieve at Lord's in 1975?

• •

8 **WHOSE** rugby tackle on a cricket pitch cost him 12 months?

---

9 **WHY** wasn't Chris Broad allowed to watch the final overs of the 1989 Benson and Hedges Cup final between Essex and Nottinghamshire?

• •

10 'As I passed forty, it dawned on me the only way I was going to play cricket at the highest level was if I ...' **HOW** did businessman David Harper actually go about achieving his ambition?

THE ANSWERS 148

23

BRILLIANT AND
BONKERS BATSMEN (2)

Batting can be a tricky business at times nowadays, but in the era of uncovered wickets it could turn into a lottery. In December 1950 Australia and England played a bizarre First Test of that Ashes series at Brisbane. The first day, a Friday, was fairly normal – Australia were bowled out for a less than impressive 228 before bad light prevented England beginning their innings. It rained all day Saturday, Sunday was a rest day and rain prevented a resumption before lunch on the Monday, by which time England prepared to bat on an archetypal 'sticky wicket'. At 68–7, England's skipper Freddie Brown declared, 160 runs behind, reasoning that the longer England batted the more time it gave the pitch to improve before his bowlers could have another go at Australia. Then at 32–7 Aussie captain Lindsay Hassett had the same idea and also declared, before reducing England to 30–6 by the close. Although the wicket was easier on the Tuesday, it wasn't enough to save England, who were bowled out for 122.

Here are some more bewildering batting facts to test your wits.

1 In 1993, Sussex scored 1,536 runs in four innings – two one-day matches and a County Championship game – an impressive average of 384 per innings. **HOW** many of these three matches did they lose?

---

2 Intended to produce a definitive result, **WHO** won the famous 'Timeless Test' (it actually lasted for ten playing days) played at the end of England's tour of South Africa in 1939?

• •

3 **HOW** many runs had Len Hutton scored for Yorkshire against Leicestershire on 25 May 1946, causing radio announcer John Snagge to erroneously inform the listeners that he was unwell?

---

4 Many people will remember that Glamorgan's Malcolm Nash bowled the famous over that Gary Sobers hit for 36 runs in 1968. But **WHO** nearly spoiled the party by catching the fifth 6, only to fall backwards over the boundary rope?

5 Twenty-five cricketers have scored 100 or more first-class centuries; only two have reached that landmark in a Test match. **WHO** are they, and **WHY** was one particularly serendipitous timing?

•••

6 Normally in cricket, everyone but the captain with the responsibility for the decision wants the skipper to make a braver declaration than he does. But **WHY** did the Australia team want Mark Taylor to postpone his declaration in the Second Test versus Pakistan at Peshawar in 1998?

───

7 **WHY** could Aravinda de Silva have been forgiven for being a little stiff when he came out to bat at Columbo for Sri Lanka against India in 1997?

•••

8 The feat of scoring 1,000 runs in an English cricket season before the end of May is a rare feat. **WHO** was the last person to achieve it, and what percentage of his runs came from his top score?

9 Only seven batsmen, in fact, have scored 1,000 runs in May in an English season, including the three greats below. **WHICH** one of them is the only player to have done it twice?

(A) W.G. Grace
(B) Don Bradman
(C) Wally Hammond

---

10 When Durham wicketkeeper Chris Scott dropped the opposition star batsman for 18 he remarked, 'I hope he doesn't go on and get a hundred.' **WHO** was the batsman?

(A) Brian Lara
(B) Chris Gayle
(C) Kevin Pietersen

THE ANSWERS 150

24

STRANGE RULES AND DUMB DISMISSALS

There is stiff competition as to what is the strangest dismissal in Test cricket, but perhaps none as odd as Andrew 'Freddie' Flintoff's claim in his autobiography that he was once run out because the after-effects of the Viagra he'd overindulged in the night before had left him unable to run properly. Hard on the heels of this would be Dean Jones's dismissal in Georgetown, Guyana, in 1991. After being clean-bowled Jones headed up the pitch for the pavilion, not realising the umpire had called 'no-ball'. A West Indies fielder grabbed the ball and pulled out a remaining stump and Jones was – incorrectly, as it turned out later – given as run out.

Since 2017, when updates to the Laws of the Game brought 'handling the ball' under 'obstructing the field', there are now only nine different ways of getting out (no, I'm not telling you what they are – this is a quiz book, you tell me!). But some players don't need unusual methods of dismissal to get out in a strange way … and that's before some of the odd rules applied in certain games are taken into account.

1 **WHY** did Muttiah Muralitharan regret going to congratulate Kumar Sangakkara on his century at Christchurch in 2006?

2 **WHICH** player was bowled from *behind* his stumps when batting for Warwickshire versus Middlesex in 1948? And **WHAT** else was unusual about his international career?

3 **HOW** can a team dismiss the opposition with only one ball remaining if they still have four wickets left *and* all the wickets must fall in a different manner (so no running someone out off three consecutive no-balls, for example)?

4 **WHO** once took a catch while 'blindfolded'?

5 A 1955 match took place between politicians and actors, featuring future prime minister (then foreign secretary) Harold MacMillan and famous luvvie Richard Attenborough, who misjudged a catch on the boundary and ended up in hospital with a bashed-in nose! But **WHAT** would a bowler get for dismissing an opposition batsman for a duck under the match rules?

---

6 Not counting running out the non-striking batsman backing up, **HOW** can a bowler take a wicket without delivering the ball?

● ●

7 In 1904, you would have been very unpopular with your teammates for being unable to resist clearing the boundary with a shot. **WHO** would your team have been comprised of?

(A) Soldiers
(B) Sailors
(C) Military policemen

---

8 **HOW**, in May 1775, did Edward 'Lumpy' Stevens' bad luck change the laws of cricket? The name 'Lumpy' came from Stevens' ability to land the ball on whatever lumps were protruding from the era's poorly prepared pitches.

9 **WHO** was given out 'handled the ball' in a match in Australia with the ashes at stake?

(A) William Scotton (1887)
(B) Douglas Jardine (1933)
(C) Michael Atherton (1995)

• •

10 A batsman plays the ball short in front of him and calls for a quick single. He has taken a few steps when his partner sends him back. As he runs back to his ground, he accidentally kicks the ball onto his stumps, and the bails fall before he has grounded his bat. **IS HE** out 'hit wicket' or 'run out'? Or some other way?

THE ANSWERS 153

25

BRILLIANT AND BONKERS BOWLERS (2)

Although, as we have seen, bowlers have it easier than batsmen in that if one delivery goes awry they have the chance to put it right next time, this can work against them if they get an embarrassing attack of the cricketing 'yips'. In 1982 a young Gladstone Small was playing for Warwickshire and his first over contained ten no-balls as he desperately tried to correct his run-up. Finally a forlorn Small walked in off two paces trying to complete his over, only to bowl a wide. His captain Dennis Amiss commented, 'When I said give us three or four quick overs at the start, I didn't mean all at once!'

In our final collection of questions, here are some more from the men holding the cherry, beginning with a collection of hat-trick achievements.

1 **WHAT** connects Jimmy Matthews (England), Hugh Trumble (Australia), Wasim Akram (Pakistan) and Stuart Broad (England)? And **WHAT** distinguishes Matthews?

2 **WHAT** connects Maurice Allom (England), Peter Petherick (New Zealand) and Damien Fleming (Australia)?

3 **WHY** was Australian Peter Siddle's Test hat-trick on 25 November 2010 unique?

4 **WHAT** was strange about Merv Hughes's hat-trick against the West Indies in 1988?

5 In August 2018, **WHO** narrowly failed to achieve a hat-trick and **WHO** notched up a hat-trick in the same over when England played India at Lord's?

6 Taking four wickets in four balls is naturally a much rarer feat than a hat-trick. Only 44 have been recorded in first-class cricket to date, and none in Test matches. But **WHICH** war hero is the only player to have achieved it twice?

7 WHAT strange (and almost unprecedented) feat did New Zealand's Alex Moir achieve against England in the Wellington Test in 1951?

• •

8 When Yorkshire played Gloucestershire and then Somerset inside a week in August 1914, bowling them both out twice, HOW many different bowlers did they use in the four innings?

_____

9 A Test match opening bowler must dream of seeing their first delivery of a series end up safely pouched by second slip. WHY would Steve Harmison be an exception to the rule?

• •

10 WHAT did former England captain Colin Cowdrey do when his son Chris took his first Test wicket?

THE ANSWERS 156

★ THE ANSWERS ★

LAMENTABLE EFFORTS

1. From 1934 to 1938 they finished bottom of the table every single season. In fact after their single victory in 1935 they failed to win another match until beating Leicestershire in May 1939, a barren run of 101 games. This was also their only victory of that season, but Leicestershire were so hopeless they finished below Northants. The intervention of the Second World War meant that their win over Leicestershire was their only success in 11 years.

2. It remains the lowest completed innings in Test cricket not to have contained a single duck. Colin McCool scored 1 run, and 6 others made just 2 runs each. Perhaps strangest of all, after dismissing South Africa for 99 in their second innings, Australia won the match!

3. England were touring New Zealand when injuries to Neil Foster and Graham Dilley meant they were scratching around for a bowler. Sussex's Tony Pigott was playing for Wellington at the time and was drafted in for his debut. He was supposed to be getting married in a few days, and postponed it for a month so he could win what turned out to be his only Test cap. He took two wickets, but England were thrashed inside three days – Pigott could have made his wedding after all!

4. Captains. Mike Gatting began the summer as skipper but was sacked for non-cricketing reasons shortly after the First Test finished as a draw. The remaining four Tests were all lost under John Emburey (two matches), Chris Cowdrey and Graham Gooch.

5. 'At least that way he won't be fielding,' he said of the England team's least athletic player.

6. 34. The Railways made an impressive 910–6 declared, to which DIK replied with scores of 32 and 27 all out, for a world record defeat in first-class cricket.

7. Not a single one. W.H. Kingston came closest with a plucky 8 opening the batting in the first innings, but that was as good as it got. You won't be surprised to learn that only a single boundary was scored in the two innings as Northants replied to Yorkshire's total of 356–8 declared with scores of 27 and 15 to lose by an innings and 314 runs. Strangely, for only one of the 18 wickets to fall did the bowler require any assistance from a fielder, when Vials was caught by Myers. All the other wickets were either clean-bowled or LBW.

8. It was Surrey at Chelmsford. Surprisingly, their miserable total was the filling in a sandwich of two perfectly respectable innings: Essex's 287 and Surrey's second effort of 185–2.

9. Astonishingly, England (45 and 184) beat Australia (119 and 97) by 13 runs.

10. Pugh was given out LBW for a duck. Anticipating a bouncer that never arrived, he ducked straight into a full toss that the umpire reckoned would have hit the stumps. Pugh, a colourful character, was apparently once on the shortlist to be the first James Bond after appearing in cigarette adverts on TV.

MULTIPLE-CHOICE MADNESS

1. (D) Yes, although all the first three incidents crop up elsewhere in this book, the most disgusting thing that New Zealand's prime minister Robert Muldoon had ever seen on a cricket pitch was a man bowling underarm. He had a point, though. With one ball remaining in a one-day international between Australia and New Zealand in 1981, the Kiwis needed 6 runs to tie the match. Aussie captain Greg Chappell, displaying that sense of fair play we have all come to associate with his fellow countrymen, instructed the bowler (his brother Trevor, no less) to bowl underarm along the ground, giving the batsman precisely zero chance of clearing the ropes. In another clear case of a stable door being slammed firmly shut as the horse gallops off into the distance, underarm bowling is now banned in one-day cricket.

2. (A) In a bid to encourage more ground-strokes and discourage big hitting (goodness knows what the authorities back then would have made of T20 cricket), a system was tried in which any ball *hitting* the net would add 2 runs to however many the batsmen could run, while any shot *clearing* the net would score only 3 runs in total. It didn't catch on. The illustrious Nottinghamshire batsman Arthur Shrewsbury, by now 44 years old and perhaps anticipating all the extra running between wickets that the scheme would entail – another experimental match later that month saw a player score 10 runs from one shot – sensibly absented himself from the Nottinghamshire team.

3.   (C) When it was pointed out to Swanton that the visitor was HRH, his reply was reportedly: 'Nevertheless!' Women members were finally admitted to MCC after a vote in 1999, but the 20-year waiting list means that, significant personages such as the late Rachel Heyhoe Flint and Theresa May apart, ordinary female applicants are only just beginning to be admitted now.

4.   (A) The famous lime tree at Canterbury had actually been part of the cricket ground for 158 years when it snapped in two in the 2005 gales. Any ball hitting the tree was deemed a 4, even if it would have cleared the ropes for 6, and you couldn't be caught off a rebound from its branches. Only four batsmen are recorded as clearing the 90ft (27m) tree for a legitimate 6, the last being Carl Hooper in 1992. Upon its demise, a smaller sapling was indeed planted within the boundary ropes. Sadly, from 2018 it is no longer in play due to redevelopment of the northern side of the ground. (In 2015 a spectator dived into the River Tone in Taunton, Somerset, to retrieve a ball that Chris Gayle had carelessly smashed into it, while New Road in Worcester is regularly under several feet of water during spring floods of the River Severn.)

5.   He actually did all three! Despite Northants losing eight wickets for ducks, the only player on either side to score nought in *both* innings was Dennett himself; Northants, recently admitted to the County Championship, only just reached double figures in their first innings; thanks to rain on the final day, the match was drawn.

6. (B) The gentlemen and the players did indeed change in different dressing rooms and entered the field of play through separate gates (a practice that continued until the early 1960s). On this occasion an overflowing tap from a room above the professionals' dressing room meant they found their kit soaking and unwearable when they turned up for the final morning of the match. As Yorkshire only needed 32 to win, Derbyshire agreed to take to the field in civvies for the few overs required.

7. (C) I didn't think it would be giving away too much to hint that the strangest answer here is, naturally, the correct one. The match was allocated four Saturdays to be played on from 8 March to 5 April (no day was allocated for the fourth weekend, presumably because it was Easter). The Tasmanian cricket committee, in their wisdom, also decreed that the match would not be considered over until both teams had completed their innings. So despite Break O'Day sailing past Wellington's 277 on the third day of the match, a fortnight later they all came back to finish the match. Break O'Day were by now in party mood, and their captain Charles Eady, who also opened the batting, finished with 566, more than double the number of runs Wellington scored between them.

8. (C) Eight batsmen scored ducks in the Hampshire first innings, but none did in the second. Whether they received a rocket from captain Lionel Tennyson, who was presumably beyond criticism after his impressive first-innings score of 4, is not recorded, but something did the trick. Tennyson

was the grandson of Alfred, the 19th-century poet laureate, and later published his memoirs under the title *From Verse to Worse*. Despite a better showing following on, it still looked grim when Hampshire's eighth wicket fell with them only 66 runs ahead. Enter Walter Livsey, Tennyson's valet, who scored an unbeaten century in stands of 177 and 70 for the last two wickets. A demoralised Warwickshire understandably struggled, and Hampshire won by 155 runs.

9. (C) Bert Sutcliffe (never 'Herbert', unlike his more illustrious English namesake) was no mean player himself, being capped 42 times by New Zealand and being a *Wisden* 'Cricketer of the Year' in 1949.

10. All three, in a match played at Highbury stadium in front of 8,000 spectators and, for part of it, a live TV audience. And, in a variation that was decades ahead of its time, a white ball was used.

ABNORMAL ASHES

1. The pitch had been vandalised overnight by campaigners protesting the innocence of George Davis, in jail for armed robbery. Nine months later Davis was freed by the Home Secretary. Two years after that he was back in jail, after pleading guilty to another armed robbery. No pitches were dug up this time.

2. Don Bradman. Jack Crapp was seeking to counter the widespread belief that Bradman's duck in his final Test innings, when just 4 runs would have seen him finish his Test career with the godlike average of 100, was caused by his having tears in his eyes at the ovation he received on his way to the wicket at the Oval in 1948. Crapp was at first slip at the time.

3. Aussie captain Ricky Ponting, who lost his temper after being run out by a substitute fielder going for a quick single. He was angry at England's stretching of the rules by having a specialist fielder come on as twelfth man whenever England bowlers (frequently) left the field for a change of shirt, rub down or toilet break. On this occasion, though, the sub was on quite legitimately, as Simon Jones had gone for a scan on an injured ankle. Gary Pratt, the lightning-fast young Durham cricketer brought on in his place, duly secured his place in history (and on England's victorious open-top bus ride).

4. 'If you win the toss, nine times out of ten, you should bat; the tenth time, you should have a good think about it, and then bat,' (as attributed to several cricketers down the ages). In 1951 Hutton inserted the Aussies in the First Test and watched them score 601–8 and win by an innings, but England recovered to win the series 3–1. In 2002 Hussain did the same in the First Test and Australia scored 492 and won by 384 runs – Nasser's team lost the series 4–1.

5. Ted Dexter, the chairman of selectors, who remarked afterwards, 'Who can forget Malcolm Devon?' It was understandable, really – Dexter worked his way through 29 different players in that summer's six-Test series. Four years later Ted confidently asserted before the 1993 Ashes series, 'We don't envisage chopping and changing,' and went on to use 24 players.

6. 'Count 'em yourself, ya Pommie bastard!'

7. Ladbrokes were offering 500–1 on England when they were 6–1 following on against Australia. Ian Botham's amazing 149 not out and Bob Willis's brilliant 8–43 meant that Australia players Dennis Lillee and Rodney Marsh were able to – a tad embarrassed, you would hope – collect on their £10 and £5 stakes respectively.

8. England's infamous 1932/33 Bodyline tour of Australia, when captain Douglas Jardine instructed his fast bowlers to aim short-pitched balls directly at the bodies of the Australian batsmen while packing the legside field, in an attempt to combat Don Bradman in particular. England won the series but were vilified in Australia, leading to 'leg theory' being banned in 1935.

9. Aussie bowler Dennis Lillee had come out to bat with an aluminium implement rather than a wooden one. It made a horrible noise when the ball hit it, and seemed to have the undesired effects both of damaging the ball and making it travel a shorter distance rather than a longer one. In short, everyone wanted him to change it, including his captain. Lillee's typically measured response was to hurl the offending object as far as he could towards the boundary in disgust. It had the desired effect of boosting sales of the 'ComBat', but the regulations were soon changed to stipulate that a bat's blade must be made of wood.

10. Roy Park, making his debut for Australia versus England on New Year's Eve 1920, came out to bat at number three and was bowled first ball. Australia went on to win by an innings, and Park was never picked for his country again.

IT'S NOT CRICKET

1. The bowler was Harold Larwood (who would find infamy on the Bodyline tour a few years later) and he was attempting to exact revenge after Smith had sent down several bouncers to the Notts batsmen in their innings. After a couple of rapid balls had whizzed past his nose, Smith finally got the edge that didn't quite carry. Although the keeper tried to call him back, Smith kept marching briskly and gratefully back to the pavilion.

2. Stuart Broad: he nicked a thin edge to Aussie keeper Brad Haddin, who deflected it to Michael Clarke at first slip. The umpire missed the contact and, with no reviews left, Broad survived. The Australian team, well known for always upholding the spirit of the game, were appalled, as was the Aussie nation, and singer/songwriter Denis Carnahan composed the very funny 'Why Didn't Broad Walk?'

3. (A) The council in their wisdom had decided that hard red balls had suddenly become a danger to 'people and property' and banned the playing of cricket. Uproar and a petition ensued, but the council refused to budge, leading to a protest game being organised, at which the greenkeeper took names and addresses. Five people were selected for prosecution. Whether elections or just common sense intervened, by 1933 cricket matches were reinstated.

4. They were playing for an official England XI in the infamous $20m winner-takes-all match against the Stanford Superstars, and lost. The match itself was embarrassing

enough for the England and Wales Cricket Board, who were heavily criticised for debasing themselves before dodgy multimillionaire Allen Stanford, who funded this first – and, as it turned out, last – match of its kind. Stanford is now serving a 110-year sentence in the US for fraud.

5. Colin Croft was bowling for the Windies and Fred Goodall was the umpire. Annoyed at some of his decisions, Croft nudged Goodall in the back as he reached the end of his run-up, almost knocking him over. Somehow Croft escaped without sanction, probably because the tour was already one of the most bad-tempered in history and no one wanted to provoke a West Indies walkout.

6. The unidentified bowler, playing for Purnell Cricket Club, for reasons known only to himself decided to deliver a deliberate no-ball straight to the boundary; the no-ball and four overthrows ended the match and the cricketing world briefly went into meltdown at this example of unsporting behaviour.

7. For allegedly enjoying a (denied) fling with a barmaid in his hotel during the First Test against West Indies in 1988. Ian Botham leapt to the defence of his friend, saying, 'It couldn't have been Gatt – anything he takes up to his room after nine o'clock, he eats.'

8. His spectacular bust-up with Pakistan umpire Shakoor Rana the previous winter. Accused by Rana of cheating by moving

his field without telling the batsman, Gatting, at the end of his tether, swore at the umpire, provoking a huge row that was only partially resolved when Gatting scribbled a perfunctory apology on a piece of paper. The consensus was that the England selectors had been looking for an excuse to dismiss him ever since.

9. With one match left in the group stage of the 55-over competition, Somerset captain Rose had worked out that (under the competition's arcane 'strike-rate' tie-break rules) if his team lost hardly any wickets in their game against Worcestershire, they would be guaranteed a place in the quarter-finals even if they lost. So, batting first, he declared at 1–0 after the first over. Uproar ensued and, though Rose had broken no rules, Somerset were thrown out of the tournament.

10. Carew Cricket Club in Wales were 21 points ahead of their nearest rivals in the league, Cresselly. They met in the final fixture, and if Cresselly could pick up 20 points for a win and a few bonus points, they could still overhaul Carew. That is until Carew declared their innings on 18–1, meaning that although Cresselly would win easily, they couldn't collect any bonus points. Pembroke County Cricket decided not to overturn the title win (as no rules had been broken), but relegated Carew for bringing the game into disrepute.

RELUCTANT RECORD-BREAKERS

1. England, unsurprisingly: 405 in 1930 (vs Australia); 400 in 2016 (vs India); 477 in 2016 (vs India); 403 in 2017 (vs Australia).

2. He became the first Test match captain to make a pair on his debut in the role. It was a costly pair, too. Pakistan won a knife-edge match by one wicket when wicketkeeper Ian Healy missed a stumping chance and instead let 4 byes to decide the issue.

3. Only three Test matches have been won by teams following on – and on every occasion the losing team has been Australia. On this occasion India's victory, after scoring a mammoth 657–7 declared in their second innings, ended a run of 16 consecutive Test wins for Australia.

4. According to CricInfo stats, if Wijesuriya, with his Test bowling average of 294.00 and a strike rate of a wicket every 586 balls (97.4 overs), bowled from both ends for a five-day Test, by the end of it the opposition would be 1,355–4 – it would take him 13 days to bowl a team out! His single wicket against Pakistan in 1985 means he has the highest bowling average in Tests.

5. In his maiden innings in Test cricket, versus New Zealand in 2017, he became the first Test batsman ever to be out 'hit wicket' first ball on debut. In his second innings he became only the sixth batsman in history to score his first Test runs

with a 6 (albeit a top edge). Then in the first innings of the Second Test he hit his wicket again, becoming the first batsman to be out in this unusual manner in consecutive Tests. And in the second innings he retired hurt after a rising ball broke his arm!

6. Warwickshire and England's Andy Lloyd, who made his England debut against the West Indies in June 1984. Half an hour into his first innings, with 10 runs to his name, he was hit on the head by Malcolm Marshall; his helmet did not protect him sufficiently from a blow that saw him spend the next few days in hospital. He didn't play cricket again that season and was never selected for England again.

7. Shane Warne, who scored 3,154 runs in his 15-year Test career with a top score of 99 against New Zealand in Perth in 2001 when he was caught in the deep going for glory. Why he didn't push it for the easy single that would have brought him a ton only he knows.

8. Not one. His career total of 10,342 is the highest for anyone failing to reach three figures. His highest score came in his final Test match, aged 38, when he scored 89 against the West Indies.

9. Hopwood holds the record for bowling the most balls in Test cricket without taking a wicket, sending down 462 balls against Australia in two Tests in 1934. Bopara only bowled

434 balls for England over 13 Tests, but by taking a solitary wicket in 2007 against Sri Lanka he ensured he now had a bowling average, and his final Test average was a staggering 290.00.

10. He scored the fastest known 'pair' in first-class cricket. On the final day of a tour match between Glamorgan and India in 1946, he was last man out (first ball) in Glamorgan's first innings. Glamorgan were forced to follow on, but because there was little time left in the day, they graciously waived the customary 10-minute break and started immediately, with the batting order reversed. Judge was out second ball this time, thus collecting his pair in three balls and a couple of minutes.

BRILLIANT AND BONKERS BOWLERS (1)

1. Of Test cricketers to have taken over 100 wickets, they are the only ones to have scored fewer runs than wickets taken.

2. The 'King of Spin' mugs ordered for his benefit season were initially misprinted 'Ashley Giles – King of Spain'. How many were actually produced is disputed, but Giles made the most of the publicity and embraced his new nickname.

3. Umpire Arthur Jepson – just a *little* harsh, perhaps, on someone who captured 237 first-class wickets in 407 matches, but Lloyd was only ever trusted to bowl four overs in his nine Tests.

4. (A) That is, if you're a Derbyshire bowler taking part in a 'bowl-out' against Minor County Hertfordshire in a rained-off NatWest Trophy match in 1991. An honourable mention, please, for Steve Goldsmith, the only Derbyshire bowler to hit the stumps from the five who had two attempts each. The part-time bowlers of Hertfordshire were accurate with two out of six deliveries (33 per cent) to win the match.

5. Smith was bowling. With two regular bowlers on Test duty, when another broke down in the second innings Smith decided to have a go himself, and ended with the impressive figures of 4–36.

6. (B) It was also known as the 'Bosie' to begin with, in the early 20th century. Bosanquet played seven Tests for England and was the father of ITV newsreader Reginald Bosanquet.

7. Well, not as night watchman, not in a one-day match. There were two reasons – in a match shortened to ten overs and played in pouring rain at Castleford (Bradford, Headingley and Harrogate being submerged!) they thought Fiery Fred's slogging was more suited to the run chase than Boycott's grinding. Another factor was that Boycott's spectacles would probably have been quite useless in the downpour. He switched to contact lenses the following year.

8. With Anil Kumble having taken the first nine Pakistan wickets, Srinath was very sportingly making sure his teammate got the chance to take all ten, an accomplishment he achieved in the next over by dismissing Wasim Akram. His 10–74 stands second only to Jim Laker's 10–53 against Australia.

9. Thorpe was partnering England bowler Alex Tudor in a Test match against New Zealand at Edgbaston. Tudor had come in the previous evening as night watchman with England on 3–1. On the Saturday he powered his way to 99 not out and looked to be on the verge of an improbable and impressive first Test century. With England closing in on victory and plenty of time and wickets in hand, Thorpe elected to hit the winning runs himself, leaving Tudor one short of what would have been the first Test century by an English night watchman.

10. Aussie fast bowler Glenn McGrath trod on one and injured his ankle in the warm-up. Despite being without his best bowler, skipper Ricky Ponting still invited England to bat after winning the toss. Australia bowled England out in the day – just – but England had amassed 407, achieving a momentum that would carry them through to a historic series victory.

BRILLIANT AND BONKERS BATSMEN (1)

1. England were unfortunately playing in the one-day World Cup Final. Chasing a run-rate of almost 5 (considered very high back in those days) from the start, Brearley and Boycott's pedestrian start saw the batsmen following them throw their wickets away in a desperate chase to catch up, and England went from 129–0 to 194 all out.

2. England's Alastair Cook in September 2018, after announcing his pending retirement. Needing 4 runs to end his final Test appearance with a fairy-tale hundred, Cook patiently took what he thought would be a single to cover point, but India's Jasprit Bumrah had other ideas. Never mind that no one was guarding the stumps; never mind that no one was backing up; never mind even that Cook had already made his ground almost before the ball had left Bumrah's hand; India's fielder shied at the stumps, missed by a good way and saw the ball fizz to the boundary to give Cook his landmark century.

3. Essex spinner Peter Smith, who'd had some success with the bat in his long career, was having a very dodgy season in 1947 and had bagged a pair in his previous match. No one was expecting much when he came to the crease against Derbyshire with the score at 199–9. But he bludgeoned his way to 163, still a world record first-class score for a No. 11. Thrilled by his return to form, Essex promoted him to the top five in the second innings, where he made just 4 before being caught.

4. To get his eyes used to the darkening conditions the match was concluded in. And it worked – when he went to the wicket Lancashire needed 27 from just over five overs with three wickets in hand. At the start of the 56th over the target was 25, with Hughes on strike – by the end of it Lancs needed just 1 run, as Hughes smashed John Mortimore for 6, 4, 2, 2, 4, 6 to bring the scores level and effectively win the match.

5. At 52–2, and batting with local hero Derek Randall, Boycott went for an insanely risky single. Randall sensibly stayed put until he realised Boycott had no intention whatsoever of returning to the danger end himself, at which point he set off in a futile bid to beat the ball to the stumps.

6. They are the only five batsmen to be given out officially 'timed out' – i.e. not getting to the wicket inside 3 minutes – since the stipulation was added to the laws of the game in 1980. It has never happened in a Test match or an ODI.

7. Vasbert Drakes. He was picked for Border despite being out of the country, as he was expected to arrive within a few hours of the match beginning, and Border were prepared to play a man short in the field for a while if necessary. When they won the toss and batted it seemed a good move, but a batting collapse meant Drakes was still in an aeroplane when he was timed out.

8. After watching Hussain win the toss and insert Australia only to see them score a match-winning 492, Atherton, proving once more that cricket is an easy game from the commentary box, remarked, 'I would look at the pitch, call over Nasser Hussain and ask him what he would do, then do the opposite.'

9. Seven of the wickets to fall in the match were run-outs, a Test match record. And as a proportion it was even more impressive – with two declarations, only 33 wickets fell altogether, meaning almost a quarter of the wickets fell in this manner.

10. Who else but Geoffrey Boycott, who had earlier been run out for 1 in a mix-up with Amiss.

WHO SAID?

1. (C) Robert Mugabe.

2. (C) Johnson was looking at the ordained Test cricketer Revd David Sheppard (future Bishop of Woolwich and then Liverpool). In a later match, after a succession of dropped catches off an exasperated Fred Trueman, the Yorkshire fast bowler was reported to have said, 'Kid yourself it's Sunday, Rev, and keep your hands together!'

3. (B) Not the impressively moustachioed Boon, but the grey-haired and bespectacled Steele was greeted in this way by Aussie paceman Jeff Thomson. That is, once Steele had managed to negotiate his way from the England dressing room at Lord's to the wicket, having first found himself in the basement. Brought in to counteract the fearsome pace of Lillee and Thomson, the 33-year-old Derbyshire batsman steadied the ship with four solid half-centuries that summer, earning himself a generous supply of lamb chops and steaks from his admiring local butcher. He also won the 1975 BBC Sports Personality of the Year Award. Asif Masood's run-up was described by John Arlott as looking like 'Groucho Marx chasing a waitress'.

4. (C) With Mahmud possessing a batting average of 12 and a bowling average of 64, the *New Age* certainly had a point. Inzi was a terrific and well-built batsman who, Samson-like, claimed that when he shed 17kg (37lb) after being put on a diet he stopped scoring runs. And Gatting was the famous recipient of Shane Warne's 'ball of the century' in 1993, of

which teammate Graham Gooch famously observed, 'If it had been a cheese roll it would never have got past him.'

5. 'I wouldn't say I was batting badly,' he insisted. 'I'm not batting long enough to be batting badly.'

6. England captain Michael Atherton of wicketkeeper and artist Jack Russell. In 1995 Atherton scored 185 not out in 643 minutes to save the Second Test against South Africa in Johannesburg. It looked grim for England when Jack Russell joined him at 232–5 with most of the final day left, but Jack's 29 not out off 235 balls helped England grind out an unlikely draw.

7. 'Try to win in two days. If you can't, try to lose in two days so we can have a day off.'

8. It had to be one of our cousins from across the pond, naturally, in this case comedian Robin Williams. He would probably have found sympathy from football manager Rafa Benitez, who once remarked: 'How can you tell your wife you are just popping out for a match and then not come back for five days?'

9. He was stumped second ball for 6.

10. 'Smoke 20 a day'. Phil has tried to give up several times, but so far without success.

MISCELLANEOUS STRANGENESS (1)

1. (A) Gorak Shep is near the Mount Everest Base Camp, and when Richard Kirtley noticed the resemblance (well, in his cricketer's eyes) between the plateau and the Oval, he set about arranging a charity match there.

2. In a strange (but perhaps not surprising!) approach to team-bonding, Boycott was motioning to his supposed teammates on the England balcony!

3. It was July 1944, Wyatt and Robertson were representing the RAF and the Army respectively, and an approaching German flying bomb had just gone quiet, indicating that its engine had cut out and it was about to detonate nearby. Luckily for the players, it missed the ground.

4. We're not really sure *why* he was in a generous mood, but his declaration at 92–2 on the final day, leaving England a target of 215 in 3 hours, was appreciated by the visitors, who won with seven wickets and 3 minutes to spare. As West Indies had declared their first innings at a more understandable 526–7, Sobers thus became the first Test captain to declare both innings and lose the game.

5. All were dismissed in Test cricket when their headgear (cap or helmet) fell off or was knocked off and dislodged the bails. In 1853, pre-Test cricket, England's George Parr avoided a similar fate when his hat blew off and landed on the stumps. The umpire (very carefully, one imagines) removed the hat and discovered the bails unmoved – Parr was reprieved.

6. 'Then he would have been caught in the gully.'

7. Run out. With just one eight-ball over remaining Australia needed 6 runs and had 3 wickets in hand, but they lost their final wicket from the penultimate ball trying for the winning run.

8. Bob Simpson scored 92 runs and took three wickets in the 1960 Test against West Indies, and was Australia's team coach in 1986 when they tied with India.

9. The match had already been called off by the umpires. Inzamam only took to the pitch after abandoning a lengthy protest that saw his team remain in the dressing room when England and the umpires were ready to restart after a bad-light stoppage. Pakistan felt that umpire Darrell Hair had offended their honour by penalising them earlier for ball-tampering. Hair's handling of the match was widely criticised, and he was removed from the international umpire list.

10. 1889 – the law change might have come about partly as a response to a strange match in 1887 when Surrey found themselves well ahead of Notts in their second innings but running out of time on the last day. Despairing of the Nottinghamshire bowlers' capacity to take the five remaining wickets, the Surrey captain decided to take matters into his own hands and deliberately hit his wicket with his bat. His teammates soon cottoned on, another also trashing his own stumps, two more taking a leisurely stroll down the pitch to allow the wicketkeeper to stump them, and one old traditionalist simply lobbing a dolly catch to a grateful if baffled fielder. Surrey bowled Notts out to win the match, and the authorities were forced to reconsider the rules.

BIZARRE BOOK TITLES

1. Australian spinner Arthur Mailey. Still the holder of Australia's best Test bowling figures with 9–121 in the Melbourne Test of 1921, the book's title (as well as being a nod to the 1930 classic *1066 and All That*) derives from his career-best 10–66 for Australia versus Gloucestershire later that year.

2. Steve James, former Glamorgan captain and now journalist who played twice for England.

3. Zimbabwe fast bowler Henry Olonga, who in 2003 took to the field for his country wearing a black armband, as did teammate Andy Flower, to protest against the 'death of democracy' under Robert Mugabe. The subsequent backlash led to a warrant being issued for his arrest on charges of treason, with Olonga going into exile in England.

4. Not written by a player, this is comedian Miles Jupp's interesting account of how he remarkably bluffed his way into the press box for England's tour of India in 2006.

5. The strange story of how 11 village cricketers took on the world and played the game on every continent, as told by comedy producer and cricket fanatic Harry Thompson.

6. The memoirs of former Sussex captain John Barclay, described in one review as being 'as complete a portrayal of a life spent in cricket as has been written in recent years'.

7. The subtitle of the 1994 autobiography of I.T. Botham, all-rounder extraordinaire, charity fundraiser and continual headache to his long-suffering wife.

8. The authorised biography of David Steele, the bespectacled Northamptonshire batsman who defied the terrifying Australian pace attack in 1975.

9. Ask yourself, who is always banging on about the 'corridor of uncertainty'? And who is the least uncertain pundit in cricket today? Could it be a certain Geoffrey Boycott? Indeed it could.

10. A year in the life of a cricket statistician, as seen through the eyes of *Test Match Special*'s Andrew Samson. No, I have no idea why it's called *The Moon is Toast* either …

STRANGE GOINGS-ON AT THE VILLAGE GREEN

1. (B) An Eynsham fielder spotted a couple of chaps behaving suspiciously around the team dressing rooms, and – due propriety being observed by the captain asking permission from the umpire – the team legged it off the field to catch the burglars in the act.

2. Just two: Bert Wensley of Sussex and Bill Ashdown of Kent (Wittersham is on the Kent–Sussex border). Bill and Bert bowled first, and with only one fielder available were, surprise, surprise, unable to bowl a single maiden over, but bowled out the villagers for 153. They then scored 186 before Wensley was caught out, and rain intervened to prevent a second innings.

3. (B) Scott was going along nicely when a 6 of his sailed over the ropes and hit his wife, who had just turned to walk home, smack on the head. Scott remarked, 'She probably cost me a century – I went into my shell for a while and tried to keep the ball on the ground.'

4. '… the editor.'

5. All 12 wickets that fell were caught – and every single one was a duck. In reply to Goldsborough's 5 all out (top scorer, extras 5), Dishforth made 6–2 (Bettles-Hall 5 not out, extras 1). Bettles-Hall was the only man of the 15 who went to the wicket that day to score a run.

6. The match was played 2,000ft (610m) underground in the Honister Slate Mine to raise money for Threlkeld's flood-damaged cricket ground.

7. (C) There were actually 23 ducks scored by the Farmers, but then they did have 41 batsmen, in what was not an uncommon practice for the time. One assumes they didn't all field at the same time (if they did, Yatton did incredibly well to reach 75–6 in what ended in a drawn game). The Yatton bowler Ratcliffe made Jim Laker's 10–53 against Australia look positively average by taking 11 wickets in the innings.

8. 183. For some reason unknown to me, the year before he was appointed England captain at the age of just 25, Kent cricketer Chapman decided to recruit a team of 11 workers from the Hythe Brewery to take on the Elham Division of Kent Police. The coppers batted first and were doing quite well until Chapman began bowling his 'weird slows' at them, taking four of the last six wickets. Perhaps in an attempt to impress the England selectors (well known for their attendance at local police vs brewers matches), Percy then thrashed the bowling all around the field until he was last man out, not deigning to stop for such trifling details as having already won the match when they passed 151.

9. Bramble Bank is a sandbank lying between Hampshire and the Isle of Wight that only rises enough above the tides to permit cricket at the spring and autumn equinoxes. Apparently, the unpredictable nature of the pitch means the competing teams just take it in turns to win, an arrangement that might be popular with some underperforming teams I can think of.

10. The game was played in sub-zero temperatures on a wicket of ice. It was an end-of-term match in December on a glassy field at Grantchester Meadows – there were probably more than the usual number of slips.

WHAT HAPPENED NEXT?

1. At the end of long day's batting in terrific heat, Fowler fell asleep. His partner, Mike Gatting, sensing how tired Fowler was, offered to block the final over so the centurion wouldn't have to face. Fowler recalls leaning on his bat, knowing he wouldn't need to back up or run, and counting the balls down: 'I got to three and the umpire called over!' He completed his double century the next day.

2. Steve Waugh and Jason Gillespie collided with each other; Waugh broke his nose and Gillespie his shin. It would have been a classic Laurel-and-Hardy moment if the result had been less serious. Needless to say, the catch was dropped, and the next day Australia lost the match.

3. He was dropped for 'selfish play'. His 106 runs amassed on the first day of the Test was seen as particularly galling. Recalled for the final Test of the summer, Boycott was out stumped for the first time in his Test career.

4. With the physio having already been out to treat six injuries to England batsmen (three to Alec Stewart, who remained not out), the match was abandoned because the pitch was deemed too dangerous – the first time this had ever happened. Andrew Ward put it nicely: 'Stewart must have played on worse pitches, but he was probably playing football at the time.'

5. In 1988 Australia unsurprisingly lost by an innings. That was the last time they were forced to follow on until England asked them to in 2005, a run of 190 Test matches, the longest ever.

6. (B) Despite only being 67 runs ahead of Worcestershire's paltry first innings 25, Surridge, worried about the prospect of rain, gambled on his 'spin twins' Lock and Laker with this very low declaration – and he wasn't let down. Worcestershire could only manage 40 in their second attempt, and the match total of 157 runs is still the lowest ever for a completed County Championship match. Despite the well-known bats bearing his name, this Surridge was the grandson of Percy Stuart Surridge, the founder of the cricket equipment business in 1867.

7. (B) Mr W. Hughes's lusty 70 not out allowed his partner, Cyril Smart, to complete his century and, though their 134-run stand still left them 14 shy of South Africa's first innings total, a helpful dose of rain ended the match.

8. He stayed behind to seek his fortune in the continent's goldfields but died there three years later from a fever.

9. Possibly fearing what the Australian attack would do to his batting, he put them in. After 146 overs, Australia declared on 735–6, the highest total ever posted by a side put in to bat. They won by an innings.

10. They somehow managed to lose by an innings, after India posted 759–7 and England then collapsed from 103–0 to 207 all out. It's the highest ever score made by a side suffering an innings defeat.

ODI?
OH DEAR ...

1. At the mid-game interval he told his team they still had a chance but admitted afterwards: 'I didn't really believe it. I only said it to keep their spirits up.'

2. He holds the record for his country of the most ODI centuries (28, fourth on the world list), and also of the most ODI ducks (34, top of the world list).

3. Zero. He played only one ODI, against England in 1973, and was out for a duck. His Test average was 57.78.

4. A record 277 – more than 46 overs. In what was then 60-over cricket, Canada unwisely batted first and were dismissed for 45. Even with a certain G. Boycott opening the batting, England took under 14 overs to score the runs.

5. All of them. Ireland beat them in the 2011 World Cup by three wickets; Scotland beat them in a one-off ODI in 2018 by 6 runs; and the Netherlands beat them in both the 2009 and 2014 World T20, becoming the only Associate member to beat a Test nation twice in T20s.

6. Just 25. Before fast bowler Shillingford scored a mighty 9 in the last-wicket stand of 13, the top scorer in a team boasting several Test players including Clive Lloyd was the 6 made by manager Clyde Walcott, nine years after his last Test and now in his forties. The wicket was 'sporting', but Ireland made light of it, knocking off the runs for the loss of one wicket before batting on to give the crowd some sport.

7. He is one half of the brains behind the Duckworth-Lewis method, a complicated but reasonably fair way of re-calculating the chasing team's target when time is lost to weather, first deployed in 1997. The formula runs to over 400 words on Wikipedia, so you'll just have to take my word for it.

8. They were chasing 22 from 13 balls against England in the World Cup semi-final when a brief rain shower delayed proceedings. When they returned to the field, the competition's 'most productive overs' method of recalculating the target meant that South Africa farcically now required 22 runs from a single ball.

9. In a rain-affected match against Sri Lanka, South Africa's batsman Mark Boucher got his side to 229. He thought that was enough to win them the match and qualify for the next stage of the tournament, so he played the next ball defensively. But he'd been given the wrong figures by a teammate – the match was tied, and South Africa went out.

10. More Duckworth-Lewis shenanigans, this time in Guyana in 2009. West Indies were batting against England in poor light when their Aussie coach John Dyson waved them in, believing they were ahead of the required rate. But he'd neglected to allow for the latest wicket to fall; the match was declared over and England won by 1 run.

COUNTY CRICKET

1. He scored a century in each innings, and used a runner throughout both times, having strained a thigh fielding in Warwickshire's first innings.

2. As per the existing regulation, Small was replaced by a substitute who was allowed not only to field, but to bowl and bat if needed. Warwickshire manager David Brown stepped in and took a wicket, becoming the first substitute to achieve this feat.

3. Having taken two wickets in two balls, his captain accorded his demon bowler the traditional privilege of crowding the batsmen for the hat-trick ball, whereupon McFarlane somehow contrived to bowl a wide.

4. They lost the match by ten wickets (Warks 523–4 dec. and 111, Lancs. 414–6 dec. and 226–0). And in this same remarkable match, Alvin Kallicharran and Geoff Humpage put on 470 for the fourth wicket, an English record, and Humpage equalled the English record of sixes in an inning with 13.

5. Northants made 211 all out. All ten wickets fell to catches. And each catch was taken by a different fielder. Leicestershire's Birkenshaw was the only man not to pocket a catch, though he did take three wickets.

6. Not Headingley 1981, but Taunton 1976. Gloucestershire, following on after being bowled out for 79, scored 372 in the

second innings to set Somerset a target of 119; they fell 9 runs short. Not even a young I.T. Botham could save them.

7. It snowed heavily, and play was abandoned for the day at lunchtime. Buxton is the highest market town in England, and its altitude probably played a part – the snow, which arrived after Sunday's rest day, certainly played havoc with an uncovered pitch, and Derbyshire were skittled out for 42 and 87 on the final day.

8. Probably a combination of all three. Gunn was at the wicket at half past one, the customary time for lunch, and was about to leave the field when the umpires informed him that it had been agreed on that occasion that the interval would be at two o'clock. Gunn played no shot at the next ball and let it hit his wicket, announcing, 'I take my lunch at one-thirty,' as he left the field.

9. In the first place they were trying to improve their season's slow over rate and avoid a £1,000 fine; then when it dawned on them that if they won they could win more money by finishing third in the championship they tried to 'buy' a Lancashire declaration with friendly bowling. The match was drawn but Leicestershire did avoid the fine.

10. It was the 1950s, and the distinction between amateur and professional cricketers was still being kept alive – amateurs (i.e. gentlemen) had their initials before their surname; professionals like Titmus had them after.

DUCKS GALORE!

1. Inverarity thought he'd been deceived by a very cunning delivery from Greg Chappell that bowled him, though he couldn't quite work out how, and began to trudge off the pitch with nought to his name. Then the body of a swallow was found behind the stumps – it turned out the ball had only hit the wicket after killing the unfortunate bird – and Inverarity was recalled by the umpires.

2. Ten were dismissed for a duck and one was 0 not out. Four of the Border batsmen failed to trouble the scorers in either innings.

3. 'Because that's the lowest we can put you.' Hurst holds the record for most ducks in a Test series, six in 12 innings in the 1978/79 Packer-affected Ashes in Australia.

4. He was out for a diamond duck – run out without facing a ball – after being in the middle for 26 minutes, the longest 'diamond' ever. After putting on 54 runs with Marcus Stoinis for the tenth wicket, it was also the first half-century partnership to be ended by a diamond.

5. They share the record of the most consecutive ducks in Test cricket, with five dismissals each. Agarkar's achievement was all the more spectacular, as the first four were all golden ducks and in the fifth he survived his first ball to loud cheers, only to nick his second one to the wicketkeeper, thus cementing his nickname of 'Bombay Duck'.

6. Just the 1 run, in his fourth innings, and there are some who reckon that should have been given as a leg-bye. If it had been, he would now hold the record for consecutive Test ducks.

7. Chris Martin of New Zealand, against England in 2004 and South Africa in 2013. Perhaps his running between the wickets is one reason why he failed to trouble the scorers too much.

8. Step forward again, Chris Martin – seven pairs in Tests, three more than his nearest rivals!

9. Come on down, Chris Martin. It's like *Titanic* at the Oscars, isn't it? His 71-Test career ended with a batting average of 2.36.

10. Chr– ... wait a minute? You mean it's not Chris Martin? No, it's Courtney Walsh, with 43 ducks to Martin's 36 – Walsh did take nearly twice as many Test matches as Martin to collect these, mind you. When Aussie bowler Nathan Lyon dismissed Martin with a jaffa he described as the 'best ball I've bowled', he added, '[and] I've wasted it on Chris Martin, no offence, Chris!'

STRANGE SAYINGS

1. Frank Bough

2. Fred Trueman

3. Trevor Bailey

4. Mike Gatting

5. Brian Johnston

6. Henry Blofeld

7. Tony Cozier

8. Graeme Fowler

9. Tom Graveney

10. Farokh Engineer

MISCELLANEOUS STRANGENESS

1. The man at the other end was Colin Cowdrey, and he had broken his wrist earlier in the innings. With the West Indies needing only one more wicket to win, Cowdrey came out to prevent defeat. England only needed 6 runs for victory themselves, but Allen decided discretion was the watchword, and the match ended in a draw.

2. All 17 of India's touring party took some part in the match, after some hostile bowling from the home side. Viswananth, Gaekwad and Patel were all injured batting in India's first innings, then Bedi and Chandrasekhar were hurt while fielding in the West Indies' reply. Armanath was the only 'victim' of a non-cricketing nature, rushed to hospital with appendicitis after fielding as a substitute.

3. It replicated exactly the result and winning margin in the very first Test (Australia 245 and 104, England 198 and 108) – Australia won by 45 runs.

4. 'The Sun Has Got His Hat On'. The song also gave the title to his autobiography and was his favourite choice when he was a castaway on Roy Plomley's famous desert island in 1977.

5. In the words of England coach David Lloyd, England 'murdered' Zimbabwe in Bulawayo, even though they neglected to actually beat them. The match finished as a draw with the scores level (Zimbabwe 376 and 234; England 406 and 204–6), the only time this has ever happened in

Test cricket, with England running out of time to score the winning runs.

6.   They used four different wicketkeepers in the New Zealand first innings. Their nominated keeper, Bruce French, was hit on the head by a Richard Hadlee bouncer in England's innings, so first batsman Bill Athey began behind the stumps, until Bob Taylor, who had retired two years' earlier and was at the ground working for the match sponsor, came to England's rescue for the rest of the day (the Kiwi captain Jeremy Coney having graciously agreed that England could bring on a specialist keeper). The following day Hampshire's Bobby Parks relieved Taylor, and after Sunday's rest day French was fit enough to resume at the end of the innings.

7.   Larry Gomes was on 96 not out when West Indies' ninth wicket fell, and was presumably stranded 4 short of a Test century, as Marshall had broken his left thumb while fielding on the first morning. But who should come down the pavilion steps with his wrist in plaster but the great and brave fast bowler. Gomes completed his ton, Marshall then even swished a one-handed boundary before getting out, and then, incredibly, he took seven England wickets in the second innings including a caught and bowled!

8.   It was the last time a home umpire stood in a Test match; Doug Cowie stood with Sri Lanka's Srinivas Venkataraghavan. After this match, both umpires in Test cricket would be from neutral countries.

9. As the ball he had hit looped its way towards the fielder's hands, he announced, 'I declare!'

10. Never let it be said that England didn't know how to work their way through cricket captains in the 1970s and 80s. In 1978 they were touring New Zealand under skipper Geoff Boycott after Mike Brearley had broken his arm. On the fourth day, with England needing quick runs to force a victory, Boycott was batting with his usual single-minded determination. The rest of the team were fuming in the pavilion, including vice-captain Bob Willis, who told Ian Botham on his way out to join Boycott, 'Run the bugger out.' Botham needed no further encouragement and did just that; England won the match.

HISTORY MAKERS

1. (C) In just 10½ hours, Victoria scored a world record 1,107 runs, which included a triple century from Bill Ponsford, a double century and two centuries, one from Bill Woodfull. NSW lost by an innings and 656 runs. (Ponsford and Woodfull were central figures in the Bodyline series six years later, when Australia captain Woodfull uttered the famous words to England's tour manager Pelham Warner, 'There are two teams out there. One is playing cricket and the other is not.')

2. Arthur Mailey, the New South Wales slow bowler, whose four wickets were better than any of his teammates, but his 4–362 remain the most expensive bowling figures ever recorded in first-class cricket. He said his figures would have been improved if three sitters had not been dropped, including 'two in the pavilion by a man in a bowler hat'!

3. 'You guys are history,' he apparently muttered. And, shortly afterwards, Devon made that history, bowling like a demon and taking 9–57 as South Africa were dismissed for 175, setting England on the road to victory. Malcolm's figures were the sixth best (now eighth best) in Test history.

4. The small matter of 624, a world record for any partnership in any first-class match. Neither batsman offered a chance, but Sangakkara was bowled by a no-ball while still in single figures. He made 287 to Jayawardene's 374, and had he scored 13 more runs it would have been the first time two batsmen had scored triple centuries in the same Test innings – and no one has done it since.

5. He scored a half-century and also took a catch! Heavy Monday-morning traffic prevented most of the Middlesex team from reaching Tunbridge Wells in time to resume their innings against Kent. Three made it for the start, and only one was eligible to bat, so the umpires declared their innings closed. When Kent began batting, they sportingly loaned Middlesex some players to field, and Prodger took a sharp slip catch before coming to the crease himself and scoring 74.

6. There may be others, but surely at least the joint shortest has to be two balls in a first-round match in a single-wicket tournament played at Scarborough in 1963. Derek Morgan (Derbyshire) batted first and was bowled first ball by John Mortimore (Gloucestershire). Mortimore then scored a single from the first ball he faced to win the match.

7. Each ball of his over was bowled at a different batsman – in fact his last seven consecutive balls were at seven different men. In his last 11 deliveries he took seven wickets (a world record), as a likely home win almost turned into a very strange Surrey victory; Sussex ended on 202–9. The five wickets (including a run-out) that fell in the final over was also then a world record.

8. It was scored mainly against Notts' opening batsman Norman Hill, who was bowling friendly 'donkey drops' to encourage a declaration from Leicestershire. The purists were not impressed.

9. Not quite: in 1939, Worcestershire made 130 and 142 to Somerset's 131 and 141, and 20 years earlier Somerset's 243 and 103 was matched by Sussex's 242 and 102. In the latter match, there might not have been a tie had H.J. Heygate's rheumatism not led to him being given out 'timed out' at the end of the match (he was officially recorded as 'absent hurt', as 'timed out' was only officially added to the laws of the game in 1980). He eventually limped manfully (and painfully) out of the pavilion in an attempt to win the match only to find stumps being drawn.

10. Tom Straw, Worcestershire's wicketkeeper between 1899 and 1907. Strangely, both dismissals were against Warwickshire, albeit in different centuries – the first time was in 1899 and the second in 1901.

DAFT DESCRIPTIONS

1. Aussie paceman Merv 'the Swerve' Hughes.

2. England fast bowler Bob Willis.

3. Chris Lewis (he was also dubbed 'the prat without the hat' by the *The Sun* in 1994 when he had to leave the field with sunstroke in a tour match in the West Indies).

4. Australian bowler Ernie Toshack.

5. Nottinghamshire and England's hyperactive and entertaining number three Derek Randall.

6. Indian batting genius Sachin Tendulkar.

7. The portly Pakistan captain Inzamam-ul-Haq.

8. Ian Botham, whose failure was described in Jonathan Agnew's review of the day's play as not quite getting 'his leg over'. The subsequent lengthy schoolboy giggles from Aggers and Brian Johnston apparently caused a backlog at the Dartford Tunnel as *TMS*-listening drivers found it impossible to pay the toll for laughing.

9. No opposition batsman in his right mind would have said this to his face; it was Eric Morecambe to Aussie bowler Dennis Lillee.

10. South African wrist spinner Paul Adams, who was briefly very successful until batsmen learned to ignore his unorthodox action and concentrate on the ball.

VENTURING OUTSIDE FIRST-CLASS CRICKET

1. Dorset's captain, the Reverend Andrew Wingfield Derby, faced with a Cheshire team uninterested in chasing a tough target (and probably not thinking, 'What would Jesus do?'), decided to throw them a bone by getting his bowler to deliberately bowl wides to the boundary. In this way, 56 extras were conceded in 1 over as sundries raced their way to top score. Cheshire took the bait, and Dorset won the match.

2. Nantwich cricket ground adjoins the local cemetery, which is where 16 of his shots ended up.

3. The missing player probably knew something the rest of the team didn't, as they scored a grand total of 0 all out – not even a wide or a no-ball to spoil the awful symmetry of the Ross County scorecard.

4. It was a 'family' match between 11 Graces and 11 Robinsons, related by the marriage of top scorer E.M. Grace (W.G.'s brother) and Annie Robinson.

5. (C) Local farmer Francis Trumper won the match with the help of his thoroughbred sheepdog. History does not record whether Trumper's total was rounded up …

6. A schoolboy named Stephen Fleming, playing in New Zealand for Marlborough College against Bohally School. Fleming didn't even begin to bowl until Bohally were nine wickets down in their first innings. He took a wicket first ball to finish the innings, then opened the bowling in the second

innings. From every ball in this eight-ball over he took a wicket. After Bohally survived the next over, and presumably to give them a sporting chance, Fleming was taken off, but his replacement still picked up the last two wickets and they were all out for 3.

7. He had a habit of taking out his temper on the opposition batsmen. This was sometimes through legitimate bouncers, but extended to bowling deliberate beamers, sometimes running through the crease and delivering them dangerously close. He was sent home from a tour of India for such action in 1959 and never represented his country again. On one occasion in the Lancashire League he apparently discarded the ball and picked up a stump with which to assault a batsman.

8. (A) Even Holland's own special bat, which was as wide as the wicket (surely not cricket?), was no match for the 'wicked spinning' delivery of Miss Hickling, playing for Notts Ladies against the veterans of the Crimea and Indian Mutiny. His duck was a fitting reward for his deviousness.

9. FFOP stands for Fellowship of Fairly Odd Places. This Dutch charity-fundraising team has been looking for strange places to play since 2005. In the cross-border match – their inaugural fixture – the batsmen were able to hit the ball into another country simply by playing the ball back to the bowler.

10. None. Hunt, in a one-man demolition job, scored all 49 runs needed to go past West Lothian's 48 all out.

WHAT'S IN A NAME?

1. (B) Julius Caesar, who was the son of Benjamin Caesar and Anne Caesar (née Bowler). Frederick Bowler Caesar was his brother, who also played first-class cricket. Mark Anthony are the first names of former Australian Test captain Mark Taylor.

2. (A) I'm not sure what it is about the double-O and England captains that goes together, but it was Gooch who bagged a pair on his Test debut at Edgbaston against Australia in 1975. He went on to score 8,900 Test match runs.

3. Lillee, c. Willey, b. Dilley

4. (C)… but only just. Allan Lamb was caught by Alan Kourie off Clive Rice in 1980. Cook, Mustard and Onions combined when Kent played Durham in 2007, and two Lee brothers of Somerset dismissed a third batting for Middlesex in 1933.

5. What is it about Sri Lankan cricketers and their impressive monikers? But it's not Kumar Sangakkara, Arjuna Ranatunga, Hashan Tillakaratne or Muttiah Muralitharan. Step forward, Chaminda Vaas, whose name seems concise by comparison, but Bumble was referring to his full name of Warnakulasuriya Patabendige Ushantha Joseph Chaminda Vaas. If set out in the traditional cricketing scorecard manner (W.P.U.J.C. Vaas) his initials outnumber his surname. Still, I suppose the Sri Lankans think that cricketers like Henry Dudley Gresham Leveson Gower, who captained England's 1910 tour of South Africa, had funny names too.

6. The match was the annual Authors vs Actors fixture and the three batsmen were: Arthur Conan Doyle, Alan Alexander Milne and Pelham Grenville Wodehouse, all keen cricketers. Doyle played several first-class games for MCC, Milne once wrote an ode to his cricket bat, and Wodehouse named his most famous creation after Warwickshire bowler Percy Jeeves.

7. He was knighted by the King in the Birthday Honours List, the only cricketer to have been so dubbed in the middle of a Test series. Some uncharitable observers have suggested he bought his place in India's Test match side of 1936 through nepotism and patronage. Well, Vizzy's Test batting average of 8.25 in three Tests (he didn't bowl) soon put paid to that theory!

8. Somerset's Marcus Trescothick, who hit 14 centuries for England in a 76-Test career between 2000 and 2006.

9. England spinner Monty Panesar, whose lack of talent as a fielder presumably wasn't helped by the ironic cheers that began to accompany him when he completed even the most routine stop.

10. In another classic case of nominative determinism, Edwin Boaler Alletson really was a bowler (albeit not a very good one). His 189, which included an amazing 97 runs in one 5-over period, was the only first-class century he ever scored.

BEYOND THE BOUNDARY

1. Breakfast.

2. (A) Zimbabwe's Mark Vermeulen, possibly while suffering the after-effects of a blow to the head, burned down the board's headquarters after being left out of the international squad.

3. Both had their sporting careers curtailed after car accidents cost them the sight in one eye, Milburn in 1969 at the age of 27, Banks in 1972 aged 34.

4. England wicketkeeper, eccentric and talented artist Jack Russell. He refused point-blank to don the official corporate England cap; a compromise was eventually reached whereby he stitched the England logo into his tattered old hat.

5. With England set a very gettable target of 176 to win, Pakistan decided to slow down the over rate to take advantage of the dusk that arrives quickly on the subcontinent. England were determined to stay out in the middle however dark it got, the umpires co-operated, and with Matthew Hoggard manning the sightscreen to speed matters up, England made it home in the gloom to win by six wickets.

6. The telegram purportedly from the MCC calling him up for the team was a cruel hoax. The unlucky Smith was then selected officially for an England tour of India that was called off when the Second World War broke out. He finally played four Tests for England in 1946, when he was also named one of *Wisden*'s five 'Cricketers of the Year'.

7. He became the first streaker at a Test match in England, when he interrupted proceedings in the Second Ashes Test. The famous picture of him clearing the stumps by some distance (he was understandably very keen to avoid contact) was accompanied by John Arlott's confused and disappointed response in the commentary box: 'We've got a freaker! ... Not very shapely and it's masculine.'

8. Terry Alderman was playing in the Perth Ashes Test in 1982 when a drunk English supporter invaded the pitch and whacked him on the head. Alderman hared after him and tackled him to the ground, dislocating his shoulder. The miscreant got 200 hours of community service; Alderman spent a year getting back to full fitness.

9. As an unlikely comeback by Notts gathered pace, the more superstitious of their team on the balcony decreed that everyone had to remain exactly where they were for fear of breaking the spell – which for Broad meant lying on a couch in the dressing room instead of watching the thrilling conclusion from the balcony like his teammates. It worked (!) and Notts won off the final ball of the match.

10. '... took the game to the top of a mountain.' Harper helped organise a match at the top of Mount Kilimanjaro, which broke the altitude record for a game of cricket. It took eight days to trek to the location, where international cricketers Ashley Giles, Makhaya Ntini, Heather Knight and Clare Connor took part.

BRILLIANT AND BONKERS BATSMEN (2)

1. All of them. After scoring 312 yet still losing a Sunday League game at the end of August, Sussex faced Essex in the County Championship. After making 591 first time out, when they declared their second innings on 312–3 to set Essex a target of 411 in 84 overs they must have been feeling confident. But Essex made easy work of the chase, reaching 412–3 with eight overs to spare. The match total of 1,808 was a new English match-aggregate record. Never mind, Sussex were in good batting form for the following Saturday's NatWest final against Warwickshire, and they proved it by knocking a record score for the final of 321. Unfortunately for them, Warwickshire still hadn't batted, and they immediately improved the record with a last-ball win. Sussex went away to practise their bowling …

2. It was, almost inevitably, a draw. It began on a Friday, encompassed two Sunday rest days, and day eight was a washout. At tea on day ten (a Tuesday), with England needing 42 runs to win and having five wickets in hand, the rain set in. England had a boat to catch, and the match was abandoned as a draw after 1,981 runs in 43 hours' (just over seven full days' worth of cricket) play.

3. 111. He misread Hutton's score on the piece of paper in front of him and announced: 'Yorkshire 232 all out – Hutton ill.' (In fairness to Snagge, he did correct himself straightaway!)

4. It was Roger Davis. Malcolm Nash was a seam bowler who was 'experimenting' with spin at the time. Bowling to one of the world's greatest batsmen was probably not the ideal time to try out a new technique.

5. Geoff Boycott (1977) and Zaheer Abbas (1982) are the only batsmen to have scored their 100th ton in a Test match. Boycott's was scored on his home ground of Headingley in the Fourth Ashes Test, when he also became only the fourth Englishman to be on the field for an entire Test match.

6. At the end of the second day Taylor found himself on 334 not out, level with Don Bradman's record Test score for an Australian. Overnight, he pondered whether their first innings score of 599–4 was enough to declare on, and concluded that if he were to bat on, people might wrongly assume that he was doing so merely in order to break the Don's record. So he magnanimously declared and remains forever linked with Bradman on 334. (The Test ended in a draw.)

7. The poor chap had been in the pavilion with his pads on for the small matter of 753 minutes waiting for either Sanath Jayasuriya (340) or Roshan Mahanama (225) to get out so he could go out and have a bat on the belter of a wicket. When he finally got the chance he cashed in with a century of his own out of a total of 952–6. The score was a new record, as was de Silva's patient wait.

8. It was Worcestershire's Graeme Hick in 1988, and 40 per cent of the 1,000 came in a single innings against Somerset when he scored 405 not out, somewhat overshadowing his teammate Ian Botham's return to Taunton.

9. (B) Bradman. You'd have thought that just by the number of opportunities afforded it would have been an Englishman, but Bradman achieved the feat while on tour with Australia in both 1930 and 1938.

10. (A) If it's any comfort to Scott, he is now immortalised in much the same way as Glamorgan's Malcolm Nash, in that he played a small but crucial role in a record achievement. Brian Lara had already broken Gary Sobers' Test record when scoring 375 against England earlier in 1994, and had then begun his Warwickshire career with five centuries in six innings. By wrecking Chris Scott's hope, Lara set a new world record of seven centuries in eight innings. But more memorably, he smashed an unbeaten 501 to set a new world record individual first-class score.

STRANGE RULES AND DUMB DISMISSALS

Oh, all right: bowled, caught, LBW, stumped, hit wicket, hit the ball twice, run out, obstructing the field, timed out.

1. He was run out by Brendan McCullum! The two Sri Lankans completed a leisurely single well before Chris Martin's throw came in and, having made his ground, Murali wandered down the pitch to pat Sangakkara on the back, not realising for some reason that the ball was still live. McCullum removed the bails and the umpire, quite rightly, gave him out.

2. Kiwi Martin Donnelly was facing spinner Jack Young. The ball hit his boot, bounced over the stumps, hit the ground and spun back towards him to dislodge the bails. Donnelly, who played in seven Test matches for New Zealand between 1937 and 1949, took the field for *England* in a rugby union match versus Ireland in 1947.

3. The ingenious answer provided by Andrew Ward is broadly thus: first the non-striking batsman is run out for backing up too far (i.e. before the ball has been delivered); the next batsman is timed out; the third one again backs up too far but stops the bowler removing the bails and is given out for obstruction; and the final wicket can then be taken in whichever orthodox way you prefer!

4. Alf Gover, famous for his cricketing clinics, was fielding for Surrey versus Hampshire and, after completing an over, was laboriously pulling his sweater back over his head rather belatedly at short leg. Jim Laker delivered the first ball of

his over, batsman Rodney Exton executed a pull shot and it lodged between Gover's thighs while he continued to negotiate with his jumper. Out!

5. A 1-guinea fine. One of the only two ducks was Denis Compton, 'guesting' for the actors. To avoid disappointing the spectators who were looking forward to seeing him bat, the England player (heavily disguised) was allowed to take Dickie Attenborough's place in the batting line-up and introduced to the crowd as 'Denis Pastry'.

6. By the batsman hitting his wicket before the bowler has released the ball. It happened in 1866 in a match between Sussex and Kent when George Wells was given out by the umpire, James Dean, who ruled that the ball had become 'live' as soon as the bowler began his run-up.

7. (B) Yes, cricket is a pretty difficult game to play onboard a ship, with even the gentlest swell producing variations in the wicket that would make the famous Lord's slope look innocuous. And that's before you face the issue of extremely short boundaries. Crewmen on the HMS *Irresistible* addressed the problem by erecting a seine net around the deck. The game was tip and run, and the best shot was apparently to send the ball down a hatchway, from where it could take ages to be retrieved. Woe betide you clearing the boundary net and sending the ball into the Mediterranean, though – under the ship-board rules your whole team would be given out for nought.

8. In May 1775, Kent had reduced Hambledon to 34–4 in their second innings when the famous John Small came to the wicket. Bowler Edward Stevens *three times* beat Small's bat and saw the ball pass between off stump and leg stump – and pass straight through … In those days, there was no middle stump. This glaring injustice led to a change in the laws. In May 2017 a picture was circulating online supposedly showing the result of a delivery in a Melbourne league match where the ball knocked the middle stump clean out while the bails, supporting each other, remained intact. The umpire correctly gave the batsman out as the stump had clearly been 'struck out of the ground' as per Law 28.

9. (A) The lower-case 'ashes' was a clue, sort of. Five years after the Ashes came into being following the mock obituary for English cricket published in the *Sporting Times*, William Scotton, having helped England retain the Ashes 2–0, played in an end-of-tour 'Smokers vs Non-smokers' match where one side took to the field replete with pipes and cigars. Determined to keep the ball as a souvenir, Scotton picked it up after playing the final delivery of the match. He thought the ball was dead, the non-smokers disagreed and appealed, and the umpire gave him out. It was perhaps a perfect 'Hamlet' moment.

10. The unfortunate batsman has been bowled out. The sequence of events is the same as if he played the ball onto his foot and it then ricocheted back onto the stumps. So he has effectively 'played on', which is recorded as 'bowled'.

BRILLIANT AND BONKERS BOWLERS (2)

1. The four named cricketers are the only players to take two Test hat-tricks; and Matthews is the only player to take two in the same match, against South Africa at Old Trafford in 1912.

2. They are the only cricketers to take a Test hat-trick on debut.

3. He is the only man to take a Test hat-trick on his birthday!

4. The three wickets that comprised his hat-trick were taken in three different overs. He dismissed Curtly Ambrose with the last ball of one over, then got Patrick Patterson out with the first ball of his next one to end the Windies' first innings, before trapping Gordon Greenidge LBW with his first ball of the second innings.

5. Stuart Broad just missed a hat-trick when taking two wickets in two balls. But umpire Aleem Dar bagged a hat-trick of his own by having three of his decisions reviewed in three balls – the ball before the first wicket reviewed by England, and both wickets reviewed by India – only for his verdict to be upheld every time. Well done, Mr Dar!

6. Robert 'Bob' Crisp, DSO, MC, who played in nine Test matches for South Africa in the 1930s. His four-in-fours were taken for Western Province in the early 1930s. In a remarkably action-packed life (which is well worth looking up), Crisp became the only Test cricketer to climb Kilimanjaro twice.

7.   He bowled consecutive overs in the same innings, sending down both the last over before and the first over after the tea interval. Nobody seemed to notice at the time. Thirty years earlier, Australia's Warwick Armstrong did the same after a long delay over an argument as to whether England could declare or not. The umpires finally decided they couldn't, and Armstrong, having bowled the last over before the 'declaration', began bowling again, some reckon as a protest at the delay. Again, the umpires failed to realise what was happening.

8.   Astonishingly, just two bowlers were used by Yorkshire all week in the West Country, during which time they won both matches by an innings. Alonzo Drake (a good Yorkshire name, that) and Major Booth (Major being his Christian name, not a rank – it was clearly an odd time to be a Yorkshireman) took the honours, with 23 and 17 wickets respectively. At the start of Somerset's second innings Booth was four ahead of Drake in the week's wicket-taking stakes, but Alonzo then took all ten wickets (the first Yorkshireman to do so) to forge ahead.

9.   He bowled the first ball of the 2006/7 Ashes series so wide it went straight to second slip, and it proved to be an omen for how the tour would turn out. The Aussies scored 602–9 declared, and Harmison recorded match figures of 1–177, setting the scene for a disastrous series and a 5–0 whitewash of England by Australia.

10. He was listening in his car on *Test Match Special* to Chris making his England debut in the First Test against India in Mumbai in 1984 when David Gower unexpectedly asked Chris to bowl. When Cowdrey junior bowled Kapil Dev in his first over, Cowdrey senior was so taken aback that he drove the wrong way down a one-way street.

'I tend to think that cricket is the greatest thing that God created on earth – certainly greater than sex, although sex isn't too bad either.'

Harold Pinter (1930–2008)

ABOUT
THE AUTHOR

Ian Allen is a husband, father, writer and editor from Staffordshire who has worked on many of the *Strangest* series over the last 15 or so years. He has written several awful joke books under the 'Embarrassing Dad' label and was delighted to avoid being typecast when invited to depart from these, until he learned it was to produce a similar volume called *Grumpy Old Git Jokes*. His autobiography, a work-in-progress provisionally titled *Ah Well, It's a Living*, is not expected in any bookshop soon.

He loves sport of *nearly* every kind (the allure of tennis has for some inexplicable reason eluded him), with cricket being his second favourite next to the beautiful game. It is his abiding regret that he was on a family holiday in Germany in July 1981 and thus could only follow what became one of the strangest Test matches of all time (see 'Abnormal Ashes', question 7) via intermittent and crackly World Service broadcasts. He has never forgiven his family, or indeed Germany. However, he was present at the same ground three years later to witness the events in 'Miscellaneous Strangeness 2', question 7, for himself.

He considers himself very lucky indeed that his complete lack of practical prowess hasn't prevented him from working on a wide range of sporting books. The sporting hero he identifies most closely with is C.E.J. Darbishire of *Jennings* fame, a myopic, talentless cricket nut who found solace in the role of scorer.